SCORPIONS' NEST

"Start climbing," Uncle Richard said to Stephen. "Now!"

Stephen heard the tension in his uncle's voice. It confused him. "It's only a movie," he said. "You don't have to take it so seriously."

"I said, move it!" Uncle Richard put a foot on a rock and tried to climb out. Next to his foot, a lizard stared curiously at the advancing scorpions. A tail snicked out, striking the lizard.

It fell over and twitched, then lay still. The scorpions marched over it.

"They're for real!" Stephen screamed.

"I know," Uncle Richard said.

Stephen dug his fingers deep into the dirt, as he and Uncle Richard pulled themselves up the wall of the pit. Then stone and dirt from the wall came loose in their hands. Stephen reached out for another hold, but grabbed only air.

He tumbled backward, falling to the bottom of the pit as the scorpions closed in.

Race Against Time

Watch out for more titles in the series!

RACE AGAINST TIME™

Revenge in the Silent Tomb

J. J. Fortune

Armada

First published in the U.S.A. in 1984 by
Dell Publishing Co., Inc., New York.
First published in the U.K. in Armada in 1984
by Fontana Paperbacks,
8 Grafton Street,
London W1X 3LA.

Race Against Time is a trademark of
Dell Publishing Co., Inc., New York.

Illustrations by Bill Sienkiewicz
Map by Giorgetta Bell McRee

*Special thanks to Olga Litowinsky, George Nicholson,
Bruce Hall, Betsy Gould, Beverly Horowitz and
Helene Steinhauer, from J.J. Fortune and others.*

Printed in Great Britain by
William Collins Sons & Co. Ltd., Glasgow

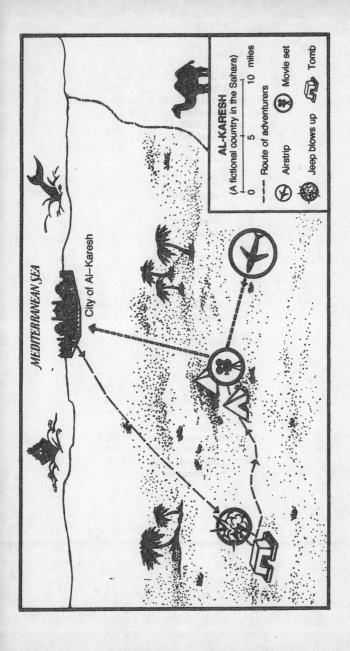

MEDITERRANEAN SEA

City of Al–Karesh

AL–KARESH
(A fictional country in the Sahara)

0   5   10 miles

- - - Route of adventurers

✈ Airstrip

☠ Movie set

💥 Jeep blows up

🏛 Tomb

CONTENTS

1

CHASE SCENE

"Bet you never had excitement like this back in New York City," Uncle Richard said as the dune buggy sped over the North African desert.

Stephen Lane didn't answer. His hands were clamped around the roll bar over his head, and his jaw was clenched in terror. The dune buggy jerked against rocks and bounced over holes, nearly throwing him out of his seat. He straightened out his long legs, bracing his feet against the floor.

"Even cab drivers don't make moves like this," he finally managed to say. "And I've had some pretty wild rides."

"Cabs don't usually have people following them," said Uncle Richard. "Turn around and look."

Stephen twisted in the seat. The wind blew his thick brown hair into his eyes, but he could see what

Uncle Richard was talking about. Two jeeps were racing after them, getting closer every second. Stephen felt sick. He recognized the pursuers—the evil-looking men he had seen at the airstrip where he and Uncle Richard had landed.

"Why are they chasing us?" he asked. "Something to do with *The Deep, Dark Secret*?"

"I doubt it," said Uncle Richard, his steely gray eyes fixed on the treacherous ground ahead. "We're in Al-Karesh. Travelers get waylaid all the time here. But I've dealt with this sort of thing before. There won't be any trouble."

Stephen looked back at the jeeps, which had moved closer. He could hear a whistle now, rising in pitch. A man stood up in one jeep, twirling a cord over his head.

A rock smacked into the rearview mirror, spraying tiny bits of glass into the buggy. Instinctively, Uncle Richard threw a hand over his eyes to shield them. The steering wheel slipped from his other hand, and the dune buggy skidded and went into a spin.

Frantically, Stephen grabbed for the wheel. It skittered through his fingers, stinging them, and he snapped his hand away in pain. The vehicle slowed down as it spun. Stephen could see the jeeps gaining behind them.

Uncle Richard's strong hands gripped the wheel again. "Nice try," he said to Stephen, and winked. He slammed his foot on the brake. The dune buggy jittered to a stop, its engine dead.

As the sand settled, Stephen heard shouting and he

turned to see the jeeps coming closer. In each jeep were three big men, so big that even Uncle Richard looked small next to them.

Suddenly Stephen was aware of the blinding sun and the desert heat, a scene he recognized from dozens of movies. If the men didn't get Stephen and Uncle Richard, the desert might.

Somewhere ahead was a camp where they would be safe. But all Stephen could see was sand, which spread evenly in all directions. The men were so close now he could hear their laughter.

"Don't worry," Uncle Richard said. "I have a plan."

This can't be happening to me, Stephen thought. I belong in New York City, watching films on my videotape player. I don't even know why these guys are after us.

It's really like a movie, he thought, remembering one he had seen with a man in a similar situation. There's just one problem, Stephen realized. The guy in the movie died.

Uncle Richard turned the ignition key. The motor sputtered and gasped and went silent.

Stephen fingered the computer watch that Uncle Richard had given him that morning. As he dabbed the controls, a compass appeared on the screen. Four tiny markers appeared on the compass. They were joined by a flashing arrow that pointed in the direction he faced.

North was ahead. The camp they'd been heading for was southeast of them.

The first of the jeeps was directly behind them now. "Do something!" Stephen shrieked, but his uncle seemed unworried. A bearded bear of a man clenching a knife in his teeth was about to jump into the dune buggy.

Uncle Richard hit the ignition switch again and pounded the gas pedal to the floor with his foot.

The engine would not start.

"Uncle Richard!" Stephen howled.

Uncle Richard jabbed the stick shift forward with a loud click. He turned the key again. With a roar the engine jumped to life.

It's too late, Stephen thought. The man with the knife landed in the back of the dune buggy.

Uncle Richard jerked at the stick shift. The buggy lurched backward and smashed into the nearest jeep. It skidded sideways and lodged on the crest of a dune, and the men in the jeep screamed and jumped out. It fell over, rolling to a stop on its side, half buried in sand.

The man with the knife wobbled on the back of the dune buggy and threw himself at Stephen with an angry cry. His meaty hand grabbed the seat back only inches from Stephen's neck. Uncle Richard slammed the stick shift as far to the right as it would go. The dune buggy spat forward, and the man waved his arms wildly and tumbled backward, landing in the sand churned up by the spinning tires.

Racing away, Uncle Richard turned southeast and headed for the camp. "There," he said, "I told you I had a plan."

Stephen stared at his uncle and groaned. "Mom never told me there was insanity in the family," he said.

Uncle Richard laughed. "Your mother doesn't know—and we won't tell her, will we? Besides, I know what I'm doing."

Maybe, Stephen thought, but he wasn't so sure. He looked back. The second jeep had driven up close to the first, and stopped long enough for the stranded men to climb on. Then it barreled after Stephen and Uncle Richard again.

Maybe Uncle Richard *does* know what he's doing, Stephen realized. The jeep was now so far behind that it would never catch up to them. He relaxed. The wind slapped his face and whipped roughly through his hair. This is a *real* adventure, Stephen thought, not just something I'm watching at the movies. For that moment he was thrilled.

The buggy zoomed over a dune, shot into midair, and turned. Stephen saw the ground ten feet beneath him, and he could hear his uncle shouting, "Jump, Steve! Move it!" Stephen stood up and dived out of the falling vehicle.

He thudded to the ground and landed on his side next to the dune buggy. He winced and opened his mouth to shout, but only a dull moan came out. He rolled onto his stomach and stopped moving.

The low whine of a motor roused him. We're finished, he thought. Brakes squealed as the jeep stopped a few feet away. In the quiet of the desert Stephen could only hear the nasty laughter of the pursuers and wondered what had happened to his uncle.

Rough hands seized Stephen's ankles and dragged him away from the buggy. A few feet away, Stephen could see Uncle Richard being dragged by another man. Uncle Richard seemed to be unconscious.

They were dumped next to each other inside the circle of men. The men began to search Stephen and Uncle Richard, looking for things to steal.

Uncle Richard opened one eye and winked at Stephen. A brief smile, and then Uncle Richard whispered, "I have a plan."

Two of the men reached for Uncle Richard's watch at the same time. It was identical to Stephen's. As their greedy fingers touched it, a light flared from the watch, brighter than the sun, and the men staggered back, blinded.

Uncle Richard's feet lashed out, tripping the man closest to him. Uncle Richard sat up and drove his elbow down on the man's chest, knocking him out. Uncle Richard grabbed the man's knife and stood up.

"Anyone tries to stop us, and they get it," he said, holding the knife out in front of him. The men backed away. "Into the jeep, Steve," Uncle Richard ordered. "Move it!"

Stephen heard a whistle as he stood up and saw a man twirling a sling. Uncle Richard hurled his knife. It slashed through the sling, but a pellet had already sped from it, and struck Uncle Richard's forehead.

He toppled forward.

As he shook himself awake the men gripped him and held him helpless. Grinning, one of the men moved a knife toward Uncle Richard's throat.

"No!" Stephen shrieked. But there was nothing he could do.

2

FLASHBACK

FRIDAY: 9:00 P.M., *New York*

Only a couple of months earlier Uncle Richard had moved into Stephen's life, taking over the top floor of the four-story Manhattan townhouse that Stephen's family owned. For years he had traveled the world over, working as an engineer. Stephen's stamp collection was filled with stamps Uncle Richard had sent from places he had visited.

Ever since their first meeting Stephen had thought there was something strange about his uncle. He had just retired from engineering, though he was only in his thirties. Stephen thought that was rather old, but he knew it wasn't old enough to be retired. Uncle Richard *did* have plenty of money though.

The mysteries surrounding his uncle didn't matter to Stephen. Despite his presence in the house, Uncle Richard didn't have much effect on Stephen's life. Not until last night . . .

"Stephen!" His mother was calling him.

Reluctantly, Stephen tore his eyes from the television and switched off the videotape player. He had been thrilled when his parents gave the videotape player to him for Christmas, but he would have been more thrilled if they gave him time to use it. Annoyed, he put his new tape, *The Caves of Gold,* on the shelf and went downstairs.

Just once he wanted to spend a Friday night watching movies without being interrupted.

"Don't frown, dear," Mom said as he entered the living room. "Is something wrong?"

"The movie's only rented for two days, so I want to watch it as many times as I can," Stephen replied. Mom looked a lot like him, tall and slim, with deep blue eyes. Then he noticed she was all dressed up. "Are you going somewhere?"

"Don't you remember?" she asked. "There's a convention of independent businesswomen in Boston. They've asked me to speak on how I plan to turn Oh, Nuts! into a chain of health-food stores."

Stephen nodded. Oh, Nuts! had taken most of his mother's time for the past year. He was happy to see her making a success of her store—but didn't understand why anyone would ask her to talk about it.

That's okay, he realized. If she's out of town, I can watch the movie in peace.

"You won't give your uncle any trouble this weekend, will you?" Stephen's father said behind him.

Stephen and Mom turned to look at Dad. Both of

them were bewildered. "Why should he give Richard any trouble?" Mom asked.

A broad smile crossed Dad's round face. He was slightly overweight and his hair was starting to thin, but that just made him look more like a schoolboy than ever.

"I have a surprise," Dad said. "I've arranged to go to Boston with you. James T. Lane and Associates has some clients in Boston. Big accounts." Dad's eyes sparkled whenever he mentioned his investment counseling business. Through hard work he had built up his service and made his name famous in the business world. "I figured I'd take the opportunity to meet them. There's a new gold deal I'm trying to put together."

"Who's going to look after Stephen?" Mom demanded.

"Richard. It's all set," Dad replied.

"*Richard?*" Mom said.

"Uncle Richard?" Oh, no, Stephen thought. It wasn't that he didn't like his uncle, but he seemed so dull. He spent most of his time going to the park and the library.

"He can handle it," Dad said. "Stephen could use a little more masculine influence in his life. I can't spend nearly as much time as I'd like to with him."

"I don't know . . . ." Mom began, but Dad pulled her coat from the hall closet and held it for her.

Just then Uncle Richard entered the room. He

stood with his hands in his pockets and looked at a spot on the wall over mother's head. "I know you're worried about Stephen. I can take care of him."

"Wait just a minute," Mrs. Lane said. "As I recall, you can barely take care of yourself."

Mr. Lane tapped his foot impatiently. "Richard is as capable as I am," he said. "They'll be all right."

"Maybe," she said. Stephen could see she wasn't convinced. "*I* always had to look after Richard . . ."

"That was a long time ago, Marion," Uncle Richard said. "Things have changed!"

"Right," Mr. Lane said. "It's settled—and besides, Stephen can take care of himself." He and Stephen grinned at each other. "Anything you want from Boston, Stephen? Some new stamps?"

"Oh, I traded my stamp collection to Larry Gleason for a great chemistry set."

"You *what*?" Mrs. Lane smiled and shook her head. "Be careful—you know the wrong combinations can be dangerous!"

"What's wrong with that?" Mr. Lane said. "*I* had a chemistry set when I was a boy."

"So did Richard," Mom said. "He burned down the garage with it."

"Only once," Uncle Richard said. "And I remember you using it when you wanted to be a werewolf."

"Now wait—" Mom said. "We're talking about Stephen. I just don't want him accidentally making explosives."

"Aw, Mom . . ." Stephen groaned.

"I will watch him, I promise," Uncle Richard said. "You have nothing to worry about. What possible trouble could we get into?"

"Trouble!" Mrs. Lane cried. "There had better *not* be any trouble!"

"You'll miss your plane," said Uncle Richard, glancing at his watch.

The phone rang, and Mrs. Lane answered it. "It's for you, Richard."

"I'll get the extension," he said, and left the room.

"Keep the chemistry set," Stephen's father whispered to Stephen. "I'll talk to your mother. She's only thinking of you, you know."

Mom rushed to the door. As she kissed Stephen good-bye, she said, "Do what Richard tells you, dear. I'll check in by phone every few hours to make sure you're okay."

"No, you *won't*," Dad said, and led her out the door. "I don't want them to spend the weekend hanging around the phone. We'll see them at one o'clock Sunday afternoon."

Stephen watched from the window as his mother and father climbed into a cab. Moments later it turned the corner and disappeared.

As awkward silence filled the room when Uncle Richard returned. They had never really spent any time alone together. Finally Uncle Richard said, "What's up, Steve?"

"There's this new videotape I got . . ." Stephen mumbled. Uncle Richard was the only person who ever called him Steve. He liked it.

"Mmm . . . *The Caves of Gold*, right?" Uncle Richard continued. "That's the one with Jack Hartford in it?"

You have to ask? Stephen thought. Where have you been? Jack Hartford was only the best and most popular actor in the world as far as Stephen was concerned. He didn't know anyone who hadn't seen *The Caves of Gold* at least once.

"Are you interested in meeting him?" Uncle Richard said off-handedly.

Stephen grinned. "Jack Hartford? Anytime! Too bad he's in North Africa filming a new movie right now."

"*The Deep, Dark Secret*," Uncle Richard replied. "Those were his people on the phone. Seems I'm wanted urgently on the set. I think you'd better come with me."

"To Africa? Okay, if you say so." Uncle Richard sure had a weird sense of humor. "I guess Jack needs an engineer on the set?"

"I'm not sure what he needs," Uncle Richard said. "But I *must* go. And I see it like this—the only way I can keep an eye on you is if you come with me."

"Uncle Richard," Stephen said slowly, "is this for real? You mean—go to Africa *this weekend*?"

"That's right. Why not?"

"Mom won't like it," Stephen said, beginning to smile.

His uncle winked. "Then let's not tell her." His laughter put Stephen at ease.

"Right," Stephen nodded. "I can see that you can't leave me on my own. I'll go to North Africa with you." He wondered how far Uncle Richard would take the joke.

Two hours later Jack Hartford's private jet was carrying them over the Atlantic Ocean, toward the tiny desert country of Al-Karesh.

"You *really* know Jack Hartford?" Stephen asked for the ninetieth time.

"Uh-huh," Uncle Richard replied. "We met in Al-Karesh, oddly enough. I taught him to fly a plane a few years back, before he got famous. Jack was better at crashing than flying. It got us in a little trouble. That's history though."

"But you were an engineer! Why were you teaching him to fly?"

"Well . . ." Uncle Richard grimaced. "I suppose you might as well know—but don't you *ever* tell your mother! I started out as an engineer, but I sort of became a . . . an adventurer, I guess you'd say."

"Wow!" Stephen said. "Like the guy Jack Hartford plays in his movies?"

"Something like that," Uncle Richard mumbled. "It's a tough life. I'm happy to be out of the business." He stared out the window of the plane.

"Adventuring makes you appreciate the little things in life—a nice bed to sleep in, three meals a day, a good watch . . ."

"I don't have a watch," Stephen said. He was angry at the change of subject, but he had the feeling that his uncle would slowly reveal the answers he wanted.

Uncle Richard fished a watch from his shirt pocket and casually tossed it to Stephen. It was thicker than most watches, with small buttons all around it. Numbers flashed across the front of it. "This is *your* watch," Stephen said, surprised.

"No, that's my spare," Uncle Richard replied.

"I thought you said you had the only one of its kind in the world."

"There are three."

"Who has the third watch?"

"They're really computers," his uncle said. "Very small, very complicated. Working it is easy though. You should have it mastered by the time we land in Al-Karesh. Go ahead and practice. I'm going to get some sleep." He stretched out in his seat and propped a pillow under his head.

With eyes closed, Uncle Richard suggested, "If you get tired of the watch, there's video equipment aboard with film cassettes."

Stephen barely heard him. He was too busy experimenting with his new gift.

Five hours later Stephen felt the plane bump to a landing. "We're here," Uncle Richard said, yawn-

ing as he came out of a nap. In New York it was
nine in the morning, but here it was two in the
afternoon.

They stepped into the hot, sandy wasteland of
Al-Karesh. Two small huts sat near the runway, with
a dune buggy parked in front of them. Beyond that
there was only desert. "We had to build the airstrip
ourselves," the pilot explained. "The movie set's a
couple miles due southwest of here." He waved his
thumb toward the buggy. "That should get you there
with no problem. Just watch out for bandits."

"Bandits?" Stephen gasped.

"Don't take him seriously," Uncle Richard had
said. But now, half an hour later, Uncle Richard was
on his knees with a bandit's knife pressing against his
throat.

Then, to Stephen's surprise, the desert began to
shake under his feet. Thunder sounded in the distance
and moved steadily closer. The men stopped laughing.
They shouted urgently to each other in a language
Stephen didn't understand. For the moment, Uncle
Richard was forgotten.

A cloud of dust moved toward them. The men
looked frightened as the thunder broke into little
rumbles. Stephen could see a dozen people on
horseback in the cloud.

Suddenly the riders spread out from a cluster to a
line and charged forward. Hoofbeats rang in the still
air. The man holding the knife to Uncle Richard's
throat dropped it and the others gasped and stumbled

backward, getting ready to run. Some of them jumped into the jeep.

Then a rider raised a rifle to the sky and fired.

Terrified and shouting, the man with the knife scrambled into the jeep. It sped away, leaving several men behind. They ran frantically after it.

Stephen watched the jeep vanish over the dune just as the horsemen circled him and Uncle Richard.

A shadow covered Stephen. His mouth dropped open in shock. Above him a slender man sat on a spotted horse. The man wore thick robes, and a hooded cloak covered his head. Scarves masked the man's face and kept Stephen from seeing anything but his green eyes. They seemed to be smiling at him.

Then he saw chains and manacles hanging from the rider's saddle.

Stephen suddenly remembered all the Tarzan movies he had ever seen. People like these had been in almost all of them.

"Slavers," Stephen said.

Uncle Richard smiled and rubbed his forehead. "Good timing," he said to the lead slaver. "I thought you'd never get here."

"You *expected* these guys?" Stephen asked.

"Of course," said the lead rider as he pulled the scarves from his face. "Richard radioed us from the plane, and we came to meet you." A mane of golden hair fell to the lead riders's slender shoulders as the scarves were pulled away. Stephen was shocked.

The rider wasn't a man. She was a beautiful woman.

"Wait a minute!" he shouted. "I know you—you've been in movies! You're . . . you're . . ."

"Lorelei Blake, meet Stephen Lane," Uncle Richard said.

"Pleased to meet you, honey," Lorelei said.

"You're *actors*!" Stephen cried.

"Of course. What did you think they were?" Uncle Richard asked.

"Well . . . um . . . slavers," Stephen mumbled. Everyone laughed.

"You watch too many movies," Uncle Richard said.

Stephen didn't think there was such a thing as "too many movies." He saw as many as he could get to, and since he'd gotten his videotape machine, he borrowed them by the basketful to watch at home. Until he had seen them all, he hadn't seen enough.

"Come on," Uncle Richard called, helping Stephen onto the back of Lorelei's horse. "We have to get to town. Move it."

A short ride later, Stephen saw a small village. The horses slowed to a trot as they rode dirt streets between crumbling buildings of gray stone. They halted in front of the largest building.

"This looks like a jail," Stephen said as he dismounted. "I thought we were going to see Jack Hartford."

"We are," Lorelei answered. "He's inside."

Minutes later a guard ushered them down the dark

halls of the jail. Ahead, Stephen saw the outline of a man standing in the gloom of a cell. The man looked only at Uncle Richard.

It was Jack Hartford.

"Thank the stars you're here," he gasped.

"Why is he *in* there?" Stephen whispered to Lorelei.

Lorelei whispered back, "Murder!"

3

THE PLOT THICKENS

SATURDAY: 3:30 P.M., *Al-Karesh*

"I didn't do it," Hartford muttered.

Stephen barely heard the actor. He had been ready to meet a powerful blond adventurer. Instead, Jack Hartford was just a man, limp and worried and all-too-human in the cell. The actor's voice should have been strong, as it was in the movies, but it was low and thin. Only the muscular body and the shock of yellow hair indicated that this prisoner and the Jack Hartford of the movies were the same man.

"You'd better explain," Uncle Richard said.

Hartford nodded. "I'm glad you came. I need someone on my side."

"How about the film crew?" Stephen asked, glowering at Lorelei. "Why aren't they helping?"

"We'll get to that," Lorelei said.

To Uncle Richard, Hartford said, "Do you remember Ian Stone?"

"Yeah, he's your stunt man," Stephen said. "I read about him in the magazines, after your movie came out."

"That's who Jack killed," said Lorelei. Stephen's jaw dropped.

"Stone?" Uncle Richard said, as if he hadn't heard Lorelei. "You worked with him around the time we rounded up Ali Ben Kir."

Stephen was bewildered. "Ali Ben who?"

"A bandit chief. He ran most of the crime in this area," Jack replied before continuing his story. "Stone and I had a falling out shortly after I went from being a stunt man to being a star. He didn't think I deserved it. He never believed we were really fighting Ali Ben Kir."

Fighting Ali Ben . . . ? Stephen wondered. There was a lot about his uncle's past that he didn't know. A thousand questions popped into his head, but he decided not to ask them until later.

"Anyway," Hartford said to Uncle Richard, "because you ducked into the woodwork, I got all the credit for the Ben Kir case. The boys back in Hollywood must have noticed. A few months after I returned to the States I got the call to play Jefferson Ross in *The Caves of Gold*."

"Which Stone just happened to be in charge of stunts on," Lorelei interjected.

Hartford's lip curled with annoyance. "Neither

one of us knew that until we were signed to do the picture," he said.

"Somebody in promotion dug up the story of our African adventure and used it to promote me."

It dawned on Stephen that he had read that story in a movie magazine, and that he had dismissed it as being so much hype. In the story, Jack Hartford led an assault on the desert fortress of a bandit, Ali Ben Kir, who terrorized an entire country. The bandit's stronghold was an ancient tomb hidden deep in the Sahara. Hartford discovered the tomb's location and stormed the fortress, eventually sending the bandit chief to jail. Stephen never dreamed the story was true, let alone that his own uncle was involved.

"So Stone was burned that you, a stunt man, were suddenly starring in a movie," he heard Uncle Richard say. "How did you feel about working with him?"

"I couldn't have been happier," Hartford said. "Stone was the best stunt man in the business. A lot better than me, anyway..I couldn't even fly a plane."

"I remember," Uncle Richard said.

Hartford ignored him. "Neither of us planned to work together after *The Caves of Gold*. All of our differences should have died right then, except that it became the hottest film of the year.

"So when the producers decided to do *The Deep, Dark Secret*, they insisted on getting together everyone who worked on the first picture. Including me and Stone."

"What was that?" Stephen whispered.

Heads jerked toward the noise from the alley outside the cell. But now the alley was silent.

"Just rats," Uncle Richard said in a disinterested tone. But his face was grim and his eyes alert. He raised a finger to his lips, signaling the others to stay quiet. Sure that they understood, Uncle Richard flagged Lorelei outside to take a look. She nodded, and vanished down the dark hallway.

"Stone was giving me lots of problems on the set," Hartford continued. Uneasy, he eyed the window. "It was no secret—everyone knew there was bad blood between us. So the night before last, Stone comes to my tent. He was loud and angry, and he'd been drinking. I guess I got a little abusive too. But he was telling me what a rotten actor I was, and how people didn't like *me*, they liked the stunts. And since he did the stunts, he should be the star of the movie. He said I didn't even deserve to be in the business."

"You got mad?" Uncle Richard asked.

"Wouldn't you?" came the reply. "Yeah, I told him he'd never work on another picture. Stone just gritted his teeth, and his face seemed to puff red. He didn't say a word. Suddenly he curled his fist and spun around and *Wham!* I'm flying across the tent. I must have been shouting my head off by then, because everyone in camp heard me. I don't remember what I said.

"Well, Stone just sneered and walked out like I was so much dirt under his heel. A couple of seconds later there was a shot outside my tent. When I got out there, Stone was dead. Someone shot him and left the gun next to the body.''

"And everyone came running and found Stone dead, and you standing over the body," Uncle Richard said.

Hartford studied Uncle Richard's hard face, and seemed to collapse into himself. He sat down on the cell's rotting cot. "You don't believe me either, do you?" he said.

Before Uncle Richard could answer, they heard a slap outside in the alley. Like a shot, Stephen and Uncle Richard dashed outside.

In the alley Lorelei stood brushing her hands together. A small figure loped around a corner at the far end of the alley and was gone.

"What happened?" Hartford shouted from his cell. "Are you all right?"

"Some beggar was listening out here," said Lorelei. "He pulled a club when I snuck up on him, so I had to get a little rough."

"You let him get away," Hartford moaned.

She smiled. "Outsiders get lost in these winding back streets. You're welcome to chase him if you like."

"Forget it," Uncle Richard ordered. "We have what we came for—Jack's story." To Lorelei, he said, "You saw Jack with the gun that killed Stone?"

"It was Jack's gun. Didn't he tell you? He bought it for protection against this Ali Ben character—figured there would be trouble, I guess. Jack's fingerprints were all over it. I hate to say it, but he's guilty."

"Oh, I don't know," Uncle Richard replied. "Those were certainly Ali Ben Kir's men who greeted us at the airstrip. Maybe Jack had a run-in with him too." He frowned. "But why kill Stone? Ali Ben Kir is strictly a thug. Framing Jack is a bit complex for him."

He turned on his heel and marched down the alley. "One thing's for sure. If the truth is anywhere, it's where Stone was killed. Would you take us there?"

"Sure," Lorelei said as she and Stephen caught up with him.

"You're pretty eager to help," Stephen said. "I thought you were against Jack."

"Let's say I want to be wrong," she replied. "But I'm not."

At the mouth of the alley a man watched them. There were teeth missing in the man's twisted smile, and a wispy beard covered his chin. Then the man's eyes met Stephen's. The face frowned and vanished into the darkness.

"Did you see that?" Stephen asked. He could feel his skin crawl. It seemed to him that the twisted man's eyes were everywhere.

"Uh-huh. Yusef," Uncle Richard said. "Ali Ben Kir's flunky. I wish we had been close enough to grab him. But there's no point in chasing him. He knows these back alleys a lot better than we do. Let's get to camp. I don't want to be in the open when Ali Ben gets the news I'm back in town."

4

SCORPIONS' NEST

SATURDAY: 4:25 P.M., *Al-Karesh*

Even in the late afternoon the desert heat was unbearable. Stephen mopped his forehead with a cloth. He noticed Uncle Richard wasn't sweating.

"How do you stay so calm?" he asked.

"Think cool, Steve. That's the secret," Uncle Richard said. Down on one knee, he studied the ground where Ian Stone had died. The shifting sands had swept over it, wiping away all traces of the dead.

"Not a clue," he said.

"We can't let Jack Hartford rot in prison," Stephen cried. "He has a movie to finish."

"I've got a plan," Uncle Richard said. Stephen hoped that was true. He was already getting the idea that his uncle's plans were usually risky; it was luck that made them succeed.

They entered Jack's tent. The air inside was sweet

and stale. Overripe fruit sat in baskets on small tables. One basket was overturned and lying on the ground. A bookshelf was knocked over and the books scattered. At the far end of the tent was a pile of pillows.

"Let's try to get a new point of view on this business," Uncle Richard said, and sat down.

His body sank into the pile of soft cushions.

Brutish hands shot out of the pillows and seized Richard around the neck. Stephen screamed.

The largest man Stephen had ever seen rose from under the pillows. Choking, Richard dangled from his hands like a doll.

He went limp suddenly. But before the other man could react, Uncle Richard jabbed his heels sharply back into his strangler's knees.

The big man howled and loosened his grip.

Gasping for air, Richard jarred forward out of the stranglehold. His hands clasped together. He turned and smashed both fists against the man's jaw.

It was a mistake. Stunned, the man rubbed his chin. He smirked at Uncle Richard.

"Get out. Move it!" Richard shouted to Stephen while dodging a massive fist. "Take out the pegs!"

Pegs? Stephen wondered. He dashed out. If Uncle Richard can't beat that guy, what can I do?

As he turned to look at the fight, his foot caught in a rope and he tumbled over. Fumbling in the sand, his hand struck wood. Stephen looked up to see one of the pegs.

Splinters dug into his fingers as he grabbed it. He

pulled. The peg didn't budge. He gritted his teeth and wrenched at the peg.

It popped out of the ground, throwing him backward.

The tent sagged where Stephen had loosened the stake. Two forms bulged against it momentarily. Stephen dashed to the tent opening to see what was happening.

He peered in. A small shape that was Uncle Richard dodged a punch from the larger shape. Uncle Richard swung wildly, clipping the giant in the side. Sweat dripped from Uncle Richard's chin, but the giant wasn't even breathing hard.

"Get away," Uncle Richard shouted as he saw Stephen. A book slid under his foot, and he fell. The giant's thick fingers stabbed down at him.

Stephen backed away. A sharp cry erupted from the tent. But the voice had an accent. It was the giant. Listening to the fight Stephen felt sick. The sides of the tent flapped over the opening and kept him from seeing what was going on. He couldn't figure out how Uncle Richard could win.

His fingers wrapped around another rope. He tugged. A second peg slipped out of the sand, and the tent looked ready to collapse. "Okay!" Stephen shouted to his uncle.

Through the crack in the tent flaps Stephen saw Uncle Richard stagger back and brace himself against the center pole. He seemed wobbly. The giant threw himself at Uncle Richard. The tent flaps blew closed.

"Come on," Uncle Richard's voice whispered from the tent. "I *dare* you!"

Something cracked like thunder. The center pole lifted into the air and toppled. Uncle Richard had tricked the giant into smashing the pole.

The tent came down.

Stephen watched bodies flounder under the canvas. Moments later Uncle Richard crawled into the open, carrying a large dictionary. He stood over the body struggling in the canvas, raised the book, and brought it down hard.

The lump stopped moving.

"Who says actions speak louder than words?" said Richard as he dropped the book. He fell to his knees, exhausted.

"What's going on here?" shouted an angry voice behind them.

Stephen looked up at a chubby American.

"I take it you're Clyde Lancer, the director of this picture. Lorelei said you'd be around here somewhere," Uncle Richard said.

"And the producer," admitted Lancer. The redness was leaving his face as he calmed down. "Don't tell me. You're Duffy, right?"

"You've got it."

"Find anything?" Lancer asked. "What's going on here anyway?"

"I was about to," Uncle Richard said, "when the walls came tumbling down."

"Oh, great," moaned Lancer. "First my star shoots my stunt man so I can't film any of the main scenes. Now I have an amateur detective hanging around."

Suddenly his eyes twinkled. "Hey," he said to Uncle Richard, "you're about Jack's size, right?"

"I guess so," Richard replied.

"How would you like to be in a movie?"

Stephen's eyes widened. "Boy, would he!" he roared, and ran to his uncle's side.

"Wait, just a minute . . ." Uncle Richard began, but he could see he was outnumbered.

"It'll be easy," Lancer said. "We don't shoot any close-ups, just long shots. We already did the upfront stuff."

"*Please!*" Stephen begged. "If the guys at school ever heard that you had the chance to be in a Jack Hartford picture and blew it . . ."

"You'll be in close with the stunt people too," Lancer said. "That's the best way to find out if anyone else had a grudge against Stone."

"All right," Richard said. "I'll do it—if Steve can do it too."

Lancer's brows rose. "Sure . . ." he said uncertainly. "What do I care? We'll let him do the run-through, and if he's any good, we'll use him when we really shoot the scene. Okay?"

Stephen smiled and nodded. "Do I get to wear a costume?"

"No," Lancer replied. "The way you're dressed will be okay for now. Lorelei!" he cried, and put his hand on Stephen's shoulder.

The actress came out of a tent.

"Give our young friend here a quick course in stunt work and acting," Lancer said. He stared at

Uncle Richard, and his brow furrowed. "The uncle looks like he can handle himself all right."

"C'mon," Lorelei told Stephen. They followed Lancer and Uncle Richard, but Stephen couldn't hear what they were saying. "It'll be a snap. And don't worry—I'll be watching the whole time."

As he walked next to Lorelei, Stephen glowed with pride, and thought, I'm going to be in a movie. . . .

A while later Stephen stood in a huge pit. He felt cheated that Uncle Richard got to wear a costume and he didn't. But Stephen was sure that Lancer would use him in the final shooting when he proved how good he was.

"Go get 'em, tiger," Lorelei called from the lip of the pit.

Nearby, Uncle Richard put on a felt hat with a wide brim. In the faded leather jacket he wore, he looked almost like Jack Hartford. At a distance, Stephen himself could not have told them apart.

"Do you think I'll win an Academy Award?" he asked his uncle.

Richard shot Stephen a look of alarm. "Forget it," he said. "Your mother is *never* going to hear about this!"

Stephen had forgotten about his mother. He could picture her reaction to this adventure. She would lock him in his room for the rest of his life, and throw Uncle Richard out of the house. He *had* to keep quiet.

"Remember," Lancer shouted through a megaphone

from the lip of the pit. "In this scene you're attacked by scorpions. They're swarming toward you, and you can't get out of the pit!"

"Got it!" Richard said. "Is this safe?"

"Absolutely!" Lancer said. "All the scorpions have had their stingers and poison removed. You couldn't be safer if you were in your own beds."

Barely able to hold back his excitement, Stephen stared around the pit. It was shaded to make it look as if it were deep underground. Green lizards scampered over boulders, unaware that Stephen Lane was about to become a star.

"Lights!" cried Lancer.

Stephen looked up. Above him the prop man was giving some money to a man with a twisted face.

"Camera!" Lancer shouted.

The twisted man looked into the pit. A vicious grin crossed his face. Uncle Richard's eyes opened wide, and Stephen felt a wave of dread.

Uncle Richard was about to speak when Lancer cried, "ACTION!"

At the far side of the pit a plastic door slid open. Behind it were hundreds of scorpions. They flooded into the pit.

"Start climbing," Uncle Richard said to Stephen. "Now!"

Stephen heard the tension in his uncle's voice. It confused him. "It's only a movie," he said. "You don't have to take it so seriously."

"I said, move it!" Uncle Richard put a foot on a rock and tried to climb out. Next to his foot a lizard stared curiously at the advancing scorpions. A tail snicked out, striking the lizard.

It fell over and twitched, then lay still. The scorpions marched over it.

"They're for real!" Stephen screamed.

"I know," Uncle Richard said.

"Get those men out of there!" Clyde roared, running around the edge of the pit.

Stephen dug his fingers deep into the dirt as he and Uncle Richard pulled themselves up the wall of the pit. Then stone and dirt from the wall came loose in their hands. Stephen reached out for another hold, but grabbed only air.

He tumbled backward, falling to the bottom of the pit as the scorpions closed in.

5

THE TWISTED MAN

SATURDAY: 5:45 P.M., *Al-Karesh*

"Stephen!" Lorelei called. "Grab my hand! I'll pull you out of there!"

His eyes fluttered open. The sun glared overhead, but he could see the dark outlines of people rushing around above him.

Lorelei's arm was stretching down at him, but it might as well have been miles away. "I can't reach," he moaned.

He was faintly aware of something crawling near his hand. Stephen grabbed a rock and smashed it down on a scorpion. He jumped to his feet as more scorpions scampered toward him. A few feet away he saw Uncle Richard, who had reached a small shelf of dirt. Uncle Richard was safe from the scorpions' stingers for a moment.

"Can you jump up to me?" Uncle Richard asked.

Stephen watched the sea of scorpions between them and shivered. "I don't know," he moaned. "Maybe if I don't move, they won't hurt me," he said.

"Jump," Uncle Richard urged. "I'll catch you."

Watching the creatures swarming near his boots, Stephen felt sick. Why couldn't he be home, watching movies? His mouth felt dry.

"I'm coming over," he said. Uncle Richard stretched out a helping hand.

What if I don't make it? Stephen thought. He took one faltering step. His heel crunched into the sea of scorpions, and Stephen felt their breaking bodies.

Poisonous tails lashed at his legs. Stephen jumped.

Uncle Richard grabbed him by the elbow. But it wasn't enough. Stephen started falling toward the scorpion sea.

Stephen swung in Uncle Richard's grip, his feet only inches from the poisonous creatures. He slammed into the pit wall.

"Sorry," said Uncle Richard. He kicked out at Stephen's leg, knocking off the scorpion that hung on Stephen's pants. Uncle Richard's heel ground down onto it.

"It didn't sting me," Stephen said, "just caught in the cloth."

Someone dropped a rope from above. Uncle Richard grabbed it and tugged.

The rope tore apart. They were trapped.

"Hold on," said Lorelei. "I'll be right back."

"Dig in," Uncle Richard told Stephen, and pulled a handful of dirt from the pit wall. He flung it at the scorpions. As it hit, they backed away. He reached for another handful of dirt. Stephen joined in.

Black drops rained down on the scorpions. "Oil," said Uncle Richard. He looked up to see Lorelei spraying the pit with it.

Richard flipped out the crystal on his watch. He stretched out his arm, and sunlight passed through the crystal. A harsh dot of light shined on the oil slick.

Below them the oil erupted in flames.

Seconds later the crew members foamed the fire out with extinguishers. Stephen and Uncle Richard stepped out on the dead scorpions. Stephen shivered as their shells crackled beneath him.

"Great! Sensational!" Clyde Lancer shouted as they were pulled out of the pit. "That's a take. We'll use it."

Uncle Richard grabbed Lancer by the lapels and pulled him close. It was one of the few times Stephen had ever seen his uncle lose his temper.

"I thought you said the scorpions were harmless," he said. "Where's the man you bought the scorpions from—the one with the twisted face?"

"H-he's around here somewhere," the chubby man stuttered.

Richard pushed him away and turned to the crew. "Spread out," he said. "Find the twisted man. I want him."

"What's so important about him?" Lorelei asked as the others left.

"That's Yusef. Ali Ben Kir's man, the one I

mentioned before," replied Uncle Richard. "Jack and I met him last time we were here."

"That fits in with what I learned in town," Lorelei said. "Ben Kir's out of prison and back in business, they think. He's lying low—no one actually *sees* him."

"If there's crime in these parts, you can see his handiwork in it," Richard said. "More and more I believe he's behind all this."

Across the camp came the sound of fighting. The twisted man ran into the clearing where they stood, a sharp knife in his hand.

"May I?" Lorelei asked.

Smiling, Uncle Richard said, "Be my guest."

Stephen was stunned. "You're letting her go out there alone?"

"Just watch," Uncle Richard said calmly.

The rest of the crew backed away as Lorelei approached Yusef. She crouched slightly and coiled like a cat.

"Come on," she said, and gestured him toward her.

Yusef lunged, his dagger aimed straight for her heart.

With blinding speed, Lorelei leaped aside. Her fingers tightened around Yusef's wrist. He screamed as she squeezed, and the knife dropped to the ground. Lorelei jolted his arm behind him.

Before he could break her grip, Lorelei pushed Yusef into Uncle Richard's waiting arms.

"Where's Ben Kir?" Uncle Richard asked.

Yusef spat.

"I know how to get answers," Lorelei said. She tightened her grip of Yusef's wrist. His dark eyes went wide with alarm.

"You wouldn't . . ." he rasped.

"What do you think Ali Ben Kir would do if he wanted answers from one of us? Hmmm?" Uncle Richard asked.

Yusef glanced from Richard to Lorelei and back. Finally his crooked body slumped. The fight went out of him.

"In the town," Yusef said. "Behind a wall of ivy . . ."

Lorelei leaned her lips to his ear and spoke in a hiss. "Did Ali Ben Kir kill Ian Stone?"

"No! No! The American—Hartford! He did it!" the twisted man cried. He shook with fear. "I don't know . . . I don't know. . . ."

"Lock him up somewhere," Uncle Richard said, and two men led the drooping Yusef away. "Get a jeep ready," Uncle Richard said to Lorelei. "We're paying another visit to Jack as soon as Steve and I have something to eat and get cleaned up."

On the way to their tent Stephen asked, "You weren't *really* going to torture that guy, were you?"

Uncle Richard shook his head. "No."

"What if he didn't talk?"

"I had a plan," Uncle Richard said, and grinned. Stephen didn't know if he was telling the truth or not.

He was still wondering when Lorelei arrived with

the jeep. He and Uncle Richard climbed on, and they headed for town.

The town seemed larger in the twilight. The moon was just rising over the horizon, and in its light the dusty streets became spooky and ominous, as if anything could leap from the shadows. Sand, wind, and time had worn the buildings smooth. They blended into one another. Stephen thought they looked like a vast, featureless wall, broken only by gloomy alleyways. Wood shutters plugged many windows, and most of the townspeople hid behind closed doors.

A townsman stood on a stone porch and watched Stephen and Lorelei with curious eyes. A woman peeked out a door behind him. Stephen began to move toward them, and they ducked inside the door, slamming it shut. Stephen could hear a bolt being pushed into place inside the door.

"Forget it," Lorelei said. "A lot of people around here act like that around strangers. They probably think we're in with Ali Ben Kir, since most strangers work with him. He sends them around to collect money. It gets pretty violent, I hear."

"Are they always like that?" Stephen asked.

"Apparently this used to be a major town, with lots of traders passing through," she said. "Until Ali Ben got out of jail."

A few buildings away, Uncle Richard pulled on the heavy wooden doors of the jail. They didn't budge. His fist pounded on the door. "Open up in there," he yelled.

A sleepy policeman shoved the door open. "Come back in the morning," he said, wiping his eyes.

Uncle Richard pushed the man aside and barked, "Now." The policeman's eyes widened. He stepped back and Uncle Richard entered. Stephen and Lorelei followed. They darted toward the cells.

Then thunder roared at them and the corridor lit up. A force like a giant hand picked Stephen up and threw him against a wall. Dirt and small chunks of plaster rained down.

As the smoke from the explosion cleared, Stephen could see dim figures moving through the cells, carrying a man.

"Jack Hartford!" Stephen shouted. "He's being kidnapped!"

6

DEN OF THIEVES

SATURDAY: 7:05 P.M., *Al-Karesh*

They leaped through the hole in the wall of Hartford's cell.

On the street a dark shape blurred at the corner of Stephen's eye. Uncle Richard's hand clasped his shoulder and shoved him to the ground, and a pipe smacked against Uncle Richard's temple.

Stephen kicked fiercely at the man attacking his uncle. The man turned and raised the pipe over Stephen's head. Rolling, Uncle Richard tripped the man, stood up, and hit him across the jaw. The rod rolled out of the man's hand and into the street. Uncle Richard touched the bruise on his forehead as he stood.

"Uncle Richard! Look out!" Stephen cried.

Uncle Richard turned. Behind him stood a man with a gun. Uncle Richard twisted out of the way as a shot rang out. Dust spattered from the street beside him where the bullet hit.

The man with the gun turned as Lorelei moved at him. She stopped.

Richard got to his feet. The man seemed confused. "You can only get one of us," Uncle Richard said. "The other one will get you. Bet on it."

The man waved the gun in front of him, pointing it first at Lorelei and Stephen, then at Uncle Richard.

Uncle Richard took a step forward. "I'll give you one chance," he said. "Let the woman and the boy go, and you can try your luck with me."

The man considered for a moment. Then he jerked his head to one side, indicating that Lorelei and Stephen should leave.

"This is crazy!" Stephen said. Uncle Richard didn't stand a chance unarmed against this man.

"I know what I'm doing," Uncle Richard said. "Take Lorelei and see if you can find the men who have Jack. I'll be along in a minute."

Lorelei took Stephen's arm and pulled him along.

"No!" Stephen said. "I've got to help Uncle Richard."

"You heard me," Uncle Richard said gruffly. "Move it!"

Glancing over his shoulder, Stephen ran down the street after Lorelei.

Stephen hadn't gotten far when he heard a shot.

"I have to go back," he told Lorelei.

"It's your decision," she said, and kept running.

The men who had Jack were barely visible in the distance, and she didn't dare take her eyes off them.

Stephen wound back through the maze, trying to remember which corners they had turned. Suddenly he heard footsteps coming toward him. Stephen's heart jumped.

A hand holding a gun poked cautiously around a corner.

I'm done for, Stephen thought. Crouching, he picked up a stone.

A man spun into the alley and pointed his gun at Stephen. Stephen threw the stone, but it flew far above the man's shoulder. That'll teach Mom to not let me play Little League, Stephen thought.

"Stephen! I told you to go with Lorelei!"

"Uncle Richard!" Stephen cried. "But . . . that shot . . . how did you . . ."

His uncle laughed. "Taking guns away from hoods is easy—when you've had enough practice at it. Our friend ran off when I shot into the air. He was running so hard he'll be in Egypt by morning.

"Where's Lorelei?"

"Oh, my gosh!" said Stephen. "I forgot about her. Come on. Move it."

Uncle Richard winced. Stephen was already running down the alley. He stopped at a turn, peering one way and then the other.

"We lost her," Stephen said. "It's all my fault. I should have stayed with her instead of coming back for you."

"Don't kick yourself over it," Uncle Richard said.

"I would have done the same for you. And Lorelei can take care of herself. The question is, what do we do now?"

"How about helping out a girl who's down on her luck?" said a voice from the shadows. Lorelei stepped alone into the dark alley, her shoulders sagging.

"They're gone," she said. "They were right in front of me and then *Poof*! Nothing."

Uncle Richard rubbed his chin. "You say they vanished right in front of you? Where?"

"In a little square about three turns down the way," Lorelei answered.

"Show the way," Uncle Richard said. "Maybe we still have a chance of finding them."

They hurried through the maze. Seconds later Lorelei brought them to a courtyard, and the maze seemed to end there. All they could see were four ivy-covered walls, and in the center of the square was an old fountain. Stephen sat on the fountain and ran his fingers across the rough stone. There hadn't been water in the fountain for years.

Uncle Richard stared at the walls. "There has to be a secret passage around here somewhere. That's the only way they could have escaped. Spread out and find that passage."

Uncle Richard and Lorelei were already testing the walls when Stephen jumped to his feet. He shoved at the nearest wall, but only hit solid stone. Angrily Stephen made a fist and rapped at the next chunk of wall, and the ivy tore away but the stone didn't move.

"We might as well give up," Lorelei said. "These walls are solid."

"NO!" Stephen shouted. "There has to be an opening here somewhere." He slammed his shoulder against the wall, and a sharp pain shot down his arm. Two steps down he threw himself against the wall again. It didn't budge.

He flung himself against the ivy a third time and passed through it. Uncle Richard and Lorelei called his name as he smacked into the ground.

Stephen looked up to see a stairway a few inches in front of him. "I think I found out where they went," he said.

"Good work, kid," Lorelei said. Uncle Richard helped Stephen to his feet and they stalked down the stairs, which led into the ground.

"Be careful," Uncle Richard said. "There might be booby traps." Stephen felt his way along the wall like a blind man. The farther down they went, the darker it got.

"Use the flashlight in your watch, Steve," Uncle Richard said.

Stephen fidgeted with the buttons on his watch as he walked. He still hadn't figured out how to work it.

He stepped into empty air and began to fall.

Stephen lunged for something to hold on to. His palm slammed on the edge of a stone, jarring his shoulder painfully. Desperately he clung to the stone.

"Help!" he cried.

Uncle Richard's watch lit up the stairwell and Lorelei grabbed Stephen's wrist. She pulled him up. The stairs had stopped where Stephen fell, and below them was a pit lined with spikes.

"A variation on the classic tiger trap," Uncle Richard said. The light from the watch revealed a slender ledge at the side of the stairs. One by one they hugged the passage wall and walked over the ledge until the stairs started again.

With even greater caution they stepped down the stairs until they reached a metal door. Uncle Richard pushed it open a crack and peered in. No light or sound came out. He signaled Lorelei and Stephen to stand out of the way.

Suddenly Uncle Richard kicked at the door, knocking it wide open, and he spun back out of the doorway.

Nothing happened.

"A trap," Uncle Richard whispered. "I can smell it."

"But there's no one there," Stephen said.

"Anyway," Lorelei said, "we can't go back. We'll have to go forward."

"You're right," Uncle Richard said as he pulled the door closed. "Take off your boots. I have a plan."

Stephen and Lorelei looked at each other in confusion. "Our boots?" they said, at almost the same time.

"Right," Uncle Richard said. "Move it."

In seconds he was holding the shoes. Carefully he

pushed at the door. The shoes fell to the floor of the room and he slammed the door shut.

THOK! THOK! THOK!

Arrows had been shot into the door. They would have gone through anyone coming in.

"Set to fire at the first step on this brick," Uncle Richard said when they were in the room. He was kneeling in the doorway dabbing at the floor.

Lorelei put on her boots and stood up. She gasped. "I'm . . . standing on a wire," she said. "It stretched as I walked on it."

"Trip wire for a bomb, from the sound of it. Don't even twitch." Uncle Richard said to Stephen, "Find the far end of the room and get down."

"Okay," Stephen called from the darkness a few minutes later.

Suddenly Richard launched himself at Lorelei, knocking her over. The two of them rolled across the floor, waiting for the big bang as the trip wire sprung up.

Instead of an explosion, a light switched on, revealing a small table. On the table lay a ring hung around a jeweled dagger.

Lorelei grew pale when she saw the ring. "It's Jack's," she said.

"Ali Ben Kir's idea of a joke. He's letting us know Jack is in his hands," said Uncle Richard. "The knife is his way of inviting us to follow."

Stephen rolled up his eyes in frustration. "Great. We don't even know where he is."

Uncle Richard was staring in the direction the dagger pointed. "Wrong," he said. The shadows from the lamplight gave him a sinister grin. "I know *exactly* where he is!"

7

TOMB OF DOOM

SATURDAY: 10:45 P.M., *Al-Karesh*

The jeep roared through the desert with Lorelei at the wheel. Somewhere ahead, Stephen knew, Ali Ben Kir waited for them in his old hideout.

"Not that I have anything against walking into traps," Lorelei shouted above the rumble of the engine, "but Jack might be dead already."

"He isn't," Uncle Richard said. "Ali Ben wants both of us. I understand that now." The face of his watch had converted to a compass. It pointed their way across the twilit wasteland.

Stephen stared at his uncle's hard face. There was nothing there that reflected what Stephen himself felt—anger, excitement, and more than a touch of fear. Uncle Richard's face was a bland mask of determination, and others might have mistaken it for indifference.

But Uncle Richard's eyes twinkled with excitement. Adventures made him come alive in a way he never was at their home on East Sixty-first Street. There he often looked lost, with no direction in his life.

But here he was strong and confident. The only crack in his coolness was the fire that flashed in his eyes when danger appeared. Just like James Bond, Stephen decided. His uncle seemed to come up with a plan for every emergency. Except the plans never seem to work exactly right, he thought with a frown. Stephen looked at his watch. If he were in New York, he'd be sitting down to dinner. And the meal on the plane was nothing to write home about.

"Tell me about the tomb," Lorelei said. "It *is* out here somewhere, isn't it?"

"Of course," Uncle Richard replied. "What's to tell? I taught Jack to fly a plane around here a few years back. He stalled the motor and crashed us in the desert about forty feet from the tomb.

"Ali Ben Kir's headquarters was there. A long time ago, kings were buried in the tomb. Now bandits use it. No outsiders ever found it before Jack and me. Ali Ben wanted to keep it that way.

"The only way we could stay alive was to blow his rackets wide open and get him shipped off to prison."

"He went back to the tomb after his release from prison?" Lorelei asked.

The drone of the tires was putting Stephen to sleep. He fought to stay awake so he could hear more.

"I think he reopened it just for us. For me. I should have destroyed it last time."

On the horizon a small mound rose from the desert floor. In the darkness it was hard to see the mound clearly. A shape passed in front of a dot of light.

"There's the place," Uncle Richard said. "At least one guard in front of it."

"Look!" Stephen said, pointing to the sky. "A shooting star!"

Uncle Richard's eyes widened and his muscles tensed. "Jump!" he screamed. He grabbed Stephen and pulled him off the speeding jeep.

They rolled for a few feet and landed next to some rocks. Uncle Richard threw himself on top of Stephen, hurting him. The shooting star arched toward the jeep.

A second later it blew up in a ball of flame and thunder.

Lorelei's thin, shaking voice came from a few feet away. "I guess we found the tomb."

"Anything hurt, Lorelei?" Uncle Richard asked.

She rubbed her elbow and flinched. "Are you kidding? There's a dead *jeep* out there!"

"That's a joke," Stephen said. "I think."

A few paces toward the tomb, what remained of their jeep quickly blackened in the fire.

"Can you get over here?" Uncle Richard asked Lorelei. "It might be dangerous. They could see you in the firelight."

She stood, and took one step. Machine-gun fire

spritzed across the sand, spraying into the air. "Not even close," she smiled as she rolled to safety at Stephen's feet.

"That tells us something," Uncle Richard said. "That was a mortar that got the jeep. If they had more, it would be raining mortars by now. So all we have to worry about is machine guns or rifles. That's no threat until we get near the tomb."

He poked his head over the rocks. "Only one guard outside, from the looks of things. No telling how many are inside. We've got a couple hundred yards to go."

"Across open desert into machine-gun fire?" Lorelei said. "Wonderful. What do we do now?"

"Uncle Richard always has a plan," Stephen said.

"We crawl," Uncle Richard said, "and we try to keep from being seen."

"*That's* a plan?"

Stephen felt a now-familiar tightening in his stomach. "I didn't say he had a good plan."

"It'll be dangerous," Uncle Richard continued. "There isn't much chance of success. You can stay here if you want, Steve."

"No way!" Stephen cried. "If I have to call Mom for a ride back from North Africa, I might as well be dead!" And I'm too scared to let you out of my sight, he added to himself.

"Take this, Lorelei," Uncle Richard said, handing her the gun. "There are twelve bullets in the pistol's clip. I want you to shoot them off three at a time toward the tomb. If I stay out of the light, the guard should be paying too much attention to you to see me—until it's too late.''

Lorelei nodded. Uncle Richard lay facedown in the sand. Like a snake he slithered into the desert. Slowly Lorelei counted to ten. She closed her eyes, taking deep breaths. ''You still there, Stephen?'' she said.

''I think so,'' he replied.

Before Stephen could say another word, Lorelei sprang up. Three shots echoed against the rocks. The shots were answered by a burst of machine-gun fire. Lorelei ducked back behind the rocks.

''What's happened with Uncle Richard?'' Stephen demanded.

''I don't know,'' Lorelei gasped. ''I was too busy to look.'' She sprang up again, fired three more shots, and dropped to the ground. Again, a staccato burst ripped the desert.

Cautiously Stephen peered over the rocks. The guard from the tomb was slowly coming nearer. At the edge of the light, a crouched figure scampered.

As if he heard something, the guard stopped suddenly. He raised the machine gun and pointed it in Uncle Richard's direction.

In a flash Uncle Richard bolted upright. The sputter of gunshots tore the air.

With a scream Stephen broke from the rocks. ''Come back!'' Lorelei hissed. He stopped running.

Uncle Richard skidded like a ballplayer sliding into home plate as his gun went off. He scooped some sand in a hand and flung it at the startled guard's face. Uncle Richard's hands gripped the guard's gun. They fell to the ground together, rolling over and over. Neither of them let go. When they stopped rolling, the guard was on top.

As Uncle Richard struggled to keep the gun barrel away, the guard pressed it against his throat. Uncle Richard looked as if his breath were being cut off. Desperately he pulled a hand from the machine gun and drove a fist into the guard.

The punch staggered the guard, and Uncle Richard kicked him away. The gun skidded across the sand. Both of them leaped for it.

The guard's hands latched on to the gun. With a grin he swung it around. The end of the barrel was inches from Uncle Richard's face.

"Drop it!" Stephen shouted from a few feet away.

For just one second the guard turned to look at Stephen. Uncle Richard gripped the barrel of the gun and slammed it hard into the guard.

A few minutes later Lorelei had the guard tied up. She handed the pistol to Uncle Richard.

To Stephen he said, "Thanks. But don't do that again. You could get yourself killed." He packed the pistol into his belt and picked up the machine gun.

The three of them stepped cautiously toward the unguarded tomb. The tiny stone gate opened into the ground. It made the tomb look just a little larger than an ordinary grave.

"That's it?" Stephen said.

"Most of it's underground," Uncle Richard replied. "You'll be surprised at how big it is."

"It's awfully quiet," Lorelei said. "That fight should have had Ali Ben's men swarming all over us. They must have heard it."

"Maybe they want us here," Uncle Richard said. "Maybe it's a trap."

A crumbling doorway led into the tomb. They stood outside for a moment.

Musty air wafted from inside the tomb. It smelled deserted, but they could see torchlight inside. They stepped in cautiously. Coffins made of clay littered the floor, but nothing moved.

No one was there.

"Looks like you made a mistake," Lorelei told Richard.

The torches flared suddenly with brilliant light, blinding them. In the glare Stephen saw the lids of the coffins shift. Scruffy men scrambled out of them and formed a circle around Stephen, Lorelei, and Uncle Richard.

The lights dimmed. Each man held a weapon trained on them.

Uncle Richard dropped the pistol and machine gun.

In the back of the chamber a wall swung open. An enormous man stood there, all bulk and power. A dark moustache wound over his upper lip, trailing back to his ears. His clothes were made from the finest silk, and rings set with diamonds and rubies glittered on his fingers. He looked like a king.

"How good of you to come, Richard Duffy," Ali Ben Kir said.

8

LAST REQUEST

"Beware of him," Ali Ben Kir warned, pointing toward Uncle Richard. "He is very tricky, that one. If he moves, shoot him."

Stephen saw a dozen eyes riveted on his uncle.

One bandit stepped forward nervously. Keeping his rifle aimed at Uncle Richard, he knelt to pick up the weapons Uncle Richard had dropped. Almost by reflex, Uncle Richard tensed, ready to spring.

Click! The rifles were cocked.

Every eye was on Uncle Richard, even Ali Ben Kir's. No one breathed. They waited for him to make his move.

Lorelei leaped into a kick, knocking over the man who was reaching for the guns on the floor.

The room exploded into action.

For one second Ali Ben Kir's men didn't know

what was happening. They shifted toward Lorelei. It was all Uncle Richard needed.

He shoved Stephen to the floor, and launched himself into a roll. His hands gripped the pistol on the floor, and he swung his legs around, knocking Lorelei off her feet.

Shots cracked above their heads. Several of Ali Ben Kir's men howled and clutched themselves where bullets hit them. Then Uncle Richard darted up and dashed at Ali Ben Kir. His arm hooked around the bandit chief's neck. Uncle Richard touched his pistol to the man's head.

"Tell them to drop their guns," Uncle Richard whispered. "Now."

Stephen couldn't believe his eyes. Thirty seconds earlier they were prisoners. Now Uncle Richard had the upper hand.

So why is Ali Ben Kir smiling? Stephen wondered. The bandits watched their leader with fearful eyes.

"Put down your weapons," the bandit leader said. "Do not think you have won, Richard Duffy. Look behind me and you will realize that no matter what you do, I will beat you."

Uncle Richard chuckled. "Nice try, Ali Ben, but I'm not taking my eyes off you for a second. Lorelei, grab a gun and keep these guys covered. Steve, take a look at what Ali Ben is talking about."

Stephen peered into the back room. It was dark. Ali Ben Kir liked his rooms dark. In the center of the room was another coffin. "Uncle Richard," Stephen said. "You better come in here."

"Lorelei, get over here," Uncle Richard ordered. "Cover my back." He turned and forced the bandit chief into the back room.

The man on the coffin rolled his head toward Stephen. "D-Duffy?" he asked. The voice was hoarse and dry.

"It's Jack Hartford," Stephen said.

"Your friend is alive," Ali Ben Kir said. "I have given him a poison that will kill him in a few hours. His strength fades already.

"I will trade his life for yours."

Uncle Richard tightened his grip on Ali Ben Kir. "I could *make* you cure him."

"No," the bandit chief answered. "You can only kill me—and then my men will kill you. I believe you call it a stand-off."

Again Ali Ben said, "Your life for Jack Hartford's."

"Richard . . ." Lorelei said, and Stephen could see the color draining from her face. She didn't have to finish the sentence. Both Stephen and Uncle Richard knew there was only one choice.

Uncle Richard dropped his arm from Ali Ben Kir's throat. The bandit chief reached up and pulled the pistol from Uncle Richard's hand.

"You, too, woman. Drop your weapon," said the bandit chief. Lorelei's gun fell to the floor.

"Shoot them," Ali Ben Kir said.

"Hold it," Lorelei shrieked. "You said Jack Hartford could go."

"Such concern for a murderer." The bandit chief's huge frame shook with laughter. "I played a trick on your friends. They once played a trick on me. That is how I landed in jail."

She scowled. "In America they say that Ali Ben Kir is a man of honor."

Ali Ben stared at Lorelei as if he were seeing her for the first time. "They speak of me in America?" he said with surprise. But Stephen saw him straighten.

"Only rumors," she said. "Whispered rumors. They call you the Lion of the Desert. You are a legend."

Stephen barely choked back a snicker. The bandit chief was stroking his moustache as Lorelei spoke. "Ali Ben Kir isn't very bright, is he?" Stephen whispered to Uncle Richard.

"He doesn't need to be," Uncle Richard whispered back. There was no laughter in his voice. "Stupid people can kill you just as dead as smart ones can."

Uncle Richard walked closer to look at Jack Hartford. Ali Ben didn't care. He was too busy listening to Lorelei.

"You are honored to be in my presence, eh?" he said, stepping toward her. "There is no need for you to die with the others. Join forces with me, and you can live."

Lorelei nodded and reached for him, slashing at his face. But before she could connect, Ali Ben's thick fingers closed around her wrist.

He flipped her aside. His smile dropped to a scowl. "This tomb will hold four bodies as easily as three," he said.

From Jack Hartford's side Uncle Richard said, "Let the boy go, Ben Kir. He's no threat to you."

"Not now, perhaps," Ali Ben replied. "But he seems much like you. One day he might return for me." In spite of himself, Stephen was pleased.

Ali Ben Kir raised Stephen to his feet. "Go over to your uncle, boy. I must get this killing over with." Lorelei took Stephen's hand, and led him to Hartford's coffin.

"Don't I get a last cigarette?" Uncle Richard asked. Stephen realized Richard's hand was hidden from view behind Hartford.

I hope he has a plan, Stephen thought. Then he remembered that Uncle Richard didn't smoke.

The bandit chief shook his head. "I do not grant last wishes." Then, smiling, he shrugged. "But I can afford to be generous. Tobacco for our friend."

He snapped his fingers. A bandit stepped forward, fishing a small pouch from under dirty rags. "NO!" Ali Ben cried. "Throw it to him. Do not go near Richard Duffy."

Uncle Richard easily caught the pouch, and placed it on the coffin. Inside the pouch was paper and coarse tobacco. Stephen couldn't understand what good that would do.

Then he saw Uncle Richard's hands. Hidden against his uncle's palm was a metal case, the clip from the gun Uncle Richard had surrendered. Uncle Richard's thumb flicked a bullet from the clip.

Stephen turned his head to see if Ali Ben Kir was watching. The bandit seemed more interested in Lorelei. Stephen himself partially blocked Ali Ben Kir's view of Uncle Richard. He stood stiffly, afraid to move.

The crystal swung out from Uncle Richard's watch. Its hard sharp edge slit the side of the bullet. Gunpower spilled across the coffin lid.

Uncle Richard began rolling a cigarette. His hands trembled so much he could barely hold the paper. Across the room Ali Ben Kir smiled at the idea of Richard Duffy being afraid. The paper slipped from Uncle Richard's shaky fingers and fell on top of the coffin. He brushed the gunpowder into the tobacco pouch as he crouched to gather up the cigarette. Stephen felt his cheeks burn with rage as the bandit chief laughed.

"We are running out of time," Ali Ben Kir joked, as he walked out of the room. "Or do you plan to kill us with old age before we kill you, eh?"

Putting the rolled cigarette in his mouth, Uncle Richard said, "Could I have some matches?" A bandit threw him a packet. He pulled out a match and struck it against the coffin.

Richard dropped the match into the tobacco pouch and hurled it into the front room at Ali Ben Kir and his men. The gunpowder and the tobacco flared up into a thick, dark smoke.

Under the cover of smoke, Uncle Richard sprang to the door separating the two rooms, Stephen and Lorelei at his side. Throwing their weight against the door, they shoved it shut as shots spattered on the stone wall near them.

"Start trying to slide the stone in the door," Uncle Richard ordered. "One of them should shift and bolt the door. If we don't keep Ben Kir out, we haven't got a chance."

The door moved toward them a half-inch. Ali Ben Kir's men were trying to open it. "Lorelei! Here!" cried Uncle Richard, and they pressed their weight to the door. "Stephen! Hurry up and find the bolt!"

Stephen's fingers moved along the stones, but nothing budged. The door opened another crack. "It's not here," Stephen sobbed. He knew they only had seconds left.

"Start pushing the stones *down*," Uncle Richard said.

Again the stones wouldn't slide. Frantically Stephen went from rock to rock. As he reached the last one, he took a deep breath and shoved.

A stone slipped to the floor and stopped. "I can't bolt it," Stephen screamed. "The door's open too far."

Suddenly Uncle Richard tugged the door open. A surprised bandit fell toward him. Richard's fist shot out and knocked the bandit backward. Lorelei and Richard threw themselves at the door, forcing it closed, and Stephen shoved the stone into place.

The door locked.

"I had planned to kill you quickly," Ali Ben Kir said through the door. "You are a fool, Richard Duffy, for you have condemned yourself and your friends to a slow death.

"For five thousand years this tomb was hidden from man. Then I discovered it, digging it out of the desert. Now I will bury you in it, and it will not be found again for another five thousand years."

Ali Ben Kir's voice grew fainter. Stephen pressed his ear against the door. "I think they're leaving," Stephen said. "I can hear lots of footsteps, all going away."

The room had gone pitch black once the door closed, and Stephen realized for the first time how near his uncle was.

A voice whispered through the rock. "I wish I could see your face as the actor dies by inches in front of you." Then the footsteps and the voice died. Ali Ben Kir was gone.

Cautiously they unbolted the door, and emerged into the outer room. Uncle Richard struck a match and held it before him. The outer room was empty, but the exit from the tomb had been closed up.

"Jack's unconscious and his breathing isn't steady, but he's alive." Lorelei said, leaning over Hartford.

Uncle Richard pressed against the exit. "Ben Kir jammed this shut. There's no way we're budging it."

"Then we're still trapped," Stephen said.

From outside came a calm, constant ticking. "Bombs," Uncle Richard growled. "He's going to bring this place down on top of us."

9

TRAPPED!

"How much time do we have?" Stephen asked.

"Until the ticking stops," Uncle Richard said.

Stephen didn't find that reassuring. "Ali Ben Kir will give himself time to get away before the big boom," Uncle Richard said. "We should be okay for about five minutes.

"Listen to the ticking for me," he said to Stephen. "If it starts slowing down, holler."

The clicks were coming four times a second.

"We need light," Uncle Richard said. His fingers dabbed at his watch. A harsh beam of light came from it, cutting a bright path in the darkness. "Photovoltaic cell. It stores sunlight," he explained. "This will hold us for a few minutes."

Uncle Richard glanced around the room until he spied a smashed urn on the floor. A dark puddle spread under it. He dabbed his fingers in the stain and raised them to his nose. "Oil," he said. "Looks like we got here earlier than expected. Ali Ben bailed out so quickly, he left supplies behind." Uncle Richard peeled off his shirt and tore it into strips.

He squatted and rubbed a ribbon of cloth in the oil. In his other hand, he took a long sliver of vase and wrapped the oily ribbon around it. Uncle Richard lit a match and it flared up against the makeshift torch. A dim flickering light filled the room.

Lorelei found some other urns in a corner. "Charcoal and saltpeter," she said. "Wonder what he was making with this?"

"Gunpowder, from the sound of it," Stephen said.

Lorelei blinked. "Where did you get that idea from?"

"I'm really into chemistry," Stephen replied. "We could blow our way out of here with that stuff!"

Uncle Richard shook his head. "And trigger whatever explosives are outside if we try. There's got to be a better way."

He passed the torch along the cracks in the walls. "I remember there being other ways out. A secret passage will cause a draft, and the draft will pull on the flame."

As Uncle Richard spoke, the fire suddenly bent toward the wall. He dropped the torch to the floor. His fingertips clawed at the edges of a stone, knocking away the dirt that had gathered in the cracks over the years. His jaw set as he slid the weighty stone out of place. It crashed to the floor at his feet.

Hundreds of round black insects skittered deeper into the hole, away from the light.

At the main door, Stephen jumped. "The ticking is slowing down," he cried.

"Forget that and come here," Uncle Richard replied. "This hole's pretty small. I can't make it through and neither can Lorelei. It's up to you."

Stephen peered up the lightless tunnel and gulped. At the edges of the torchlight the black bugs swarmed, and Stephen knew they covered the shaft. He would have to go over them. He felt sick.

"When you get to the top," Uncle Richard said, "you should be about fifty yards from the doorway of the tomb. Come around and loosen whatever's holding the door into the next room shut. We should be okay for a couple of minutes yet."

Nervous, Stephen crawled into the shaft. Tiny legs crept across his hands, and into his hair. I won't scream, he decided, and clamped his teeth together. Uncontrollable violent shivers rippled through him.

Stephen smelled fresh air above him and kept climbing. Something ahead twinkled. It looked like a star. "I made it," he called down the shaft, but his only answer was the distant flicker of the torch.

Stephen's hands hit boulders. The star was nothing more than Uncle Richard's light bouncing off a shiny streak in a rock.

The tunnel was caved in. Only insects and air could get through.

I don't have time to cry, Stephen told himself. The idea of going back down the bug-infested shaft disgusted him. Trying to forget the bugs and to focus on Uncle Richard, Stephen forced himself back down through the tunnel.

At the bottom he told Uncle Richard what he had learned. For a moment his uncle sagged as if he had given up. Rubbing at his temple, he said, "We'll have to do it your way."

Stephen listened again to the ticking. "Two ticks every second," he said. He knew the look that swept over his uncle's face in that moment—a grim, cold look. At times like these, Uncle Richard seemed more machine than man, with all his wits turned toward survival.

"Lorelei, start mixing the charcoal and saltpeter," Uncle Richard barked. His tone startled her, but she scooped up the black powder and poured it into the other jar.

"Stephen!" he said. "How much time?"

Stephen switched his watch to calculate the time. "Exactly 1.85 ticks every second," he said.

Uncle Richard dabbed at his own watch, turning on the sophisticated microcomputer hidden inside it. "We have three and a half minutes," he announced.

Sourly Lorelei said, "I don't know how good this powder will be. There's some sulfur in it, but it'll make pretty coarse stuff."

"The coarser the better," Uncle Richard replied. "We're not loading rifles here. We'll need all the raw, destructive power we can get." He pressed his ear against the exit, listening to one ticking sound, then a second, then a third. He dabbed at the computer in his watch again.

Two steps away from the exit, he said, "Here."

Stephen winced. "Here what?"

His uncle wore a confident grin, and there was a dreamy look in his eyes. "We place our cannon here," he said.

"What cannon?" Lorelei shot back. "You're *nuts*!"

Uncle Richard picked up the jar that had held the charcoal and moved it to the spot he had marked. In seconds he had poured Lorelei's gunpowder into it and was stuffing its mouth with stones and dirt. With a rock Uncle Richard smashed a small hole into the bottom of the jar. Then he took one of the oily strips he had made from his shirt, stuffed it into the hole with a few inches sticking out, and sealed up the hole with dirt.

"Our cannon," he said.

"One tick every second," Stephen said.

Uncle Richard fiddled with the computer-watch again. "Thirty seconds until the bombs go off," he said. He lit a match and touched off the cloth strip with it.

The strip began to burn toward the jar.

"Everyone into the other room," Uncle Richard shouted. "We've got to get the door shut before the bombs go off."

They darted into the room where Jack Hartford

still lay on the coffin. Lorelei stepped to take a closer look at him.

Richard yelled, "You'll have plenty of time to check him when we're finished—if this works. Right now we need to close off this wall."

"If *what* works?" Lorelei asked as she threw her shoulder against the wall, pushing the door closed. Stephen slapped the bolt into place.

Richard opened his mouth to answer.

Thunder pounded through the tomb, splintering the door around them. Uncle Richard threw himself over Stephen. The ceiling dropped dust and rubble.

The dust billowed into clouds and mixed with the smoke. Stephen raised his head to see cracks across the ceiling. But it held.

Ahead of him, a narrow streak of light shone in from outside the tomb. They were free.

Uncle Richard sprawled across him and didn't move.

Stephen shook him frantically. There was a thin gash across the back of Uncle Richard's head. "He's not breathing," Stephen cried.

"No!" Lorelei howled. She tore Uncle Richard away from Stephen and set him on his back. Propping his head back and forcing open his mouth, Lorelei pressed her lips to his and breathed air into his lungs.

As if by instinct, Uncle Richard's arm swung up behind her neck. He pulled her to him. Seconds later, Lorelei wrenched herself away, gasping.

"He *was* breathing," she said.

Uncle Richard's eyes opened, and his fingers brushed the gash. "Oooh," he said, flinching. "What happened?"

"I thought you were dead . . ." Stephen started. He saw that his uncle was no longer listening. Instead, Uncle Richard looked at the door and let out a short whoop.

"I did it!" he sighed. Calm once again, he turned toward the others. "I figured if we could cause an explosion at the exact same time Ali Ben's bombs went off . . ."

"We could use the explosions to blow a path out of here," Lorelei concluded. "Our bomb and the others would counter each other. What if it hadn't worked?"

"It worked," Uncle Richard said, stepping into the night. "We'd better get out of here. I don't want to be stuck in the desert in the morning."

"Morning!" Stephen screeched. "We've got to get back . . . Mom and Dad . . ." Fear choked the words in his throat.

"We'll make it," Uncle Richard reassured him.

Lorelei dragged the comatose form of Jack Hartford out of the tomb. "How do you suggest we get back to camp?" she asked. "Our jeep blew up, remember. And Ali Ben Kir wasn't kind enough to leave one."

"We walk," Uncle Richard said.

"You're the craziest man I ever met," said Lorelei. "It'll take hours to reach the set. The sun will come up and the heat will kill us before that. And what do we do about Jack? We can't leave him here alone."

"No," Uncle Richard answered. He picked up Jack Hartford and slung the actor over his shoulders. "None of us stays here."

"We'll die in the desert, you know," Lorelei said.

"You may be right," Uncle Richard said. With Stephen and Lorelei behind him, he trudged out onto the sands.

10

THE ENDLESS DESERT

SUNDAY: 4:30 A.M., *Al-Karesh*

For two hours they marched through the desert.

The sun was a sliver on the horizon, dim against the pale gray sky. Worse, Stephen felt time slipping away with every step. If he was reading his watch right, they had less than 14 hours to get all the way to Manhattan before his parents got home. By Stephen's calculations, that was barely enough time— even if they didn't get into any more danger.

His tongue stuck to the roof of his mouth. Stephen swallowed, and his throat seemed to crack with dust. He thought of himself as Peter O'Toole in *Lawrence of Arabia*, staggering for days through an endless desert, sun and sand pounding at him as he hopelessly searched for water that would never be found.

Oh, great, Stephen said to himself. Keep thinking about stuff like that and you might as well give up.

But no matter how he tried to keep them away, images of scorched faces and blistered lips kept leaping into his head. He lightly touched his mouth with a finger, afraid that he already looked like that.

A few paces behind Stephen, Lorelei and Uncle Richard dragged Jack Hartford. The actor had a fever. It was made worse by the heat that oppressed them all. From time to time Hartford's lips parted for a bloodcurdling moan, but that was the only sound he made. Like his breathing, his pulse was unsteady. It was clear that he was dying.

"We can't go on like this," Lorelei began, but a withering glance from Uncle Richard silenced her.

"I'm so thirsty," Stephen said. "Isn't there some way to get water?"

"Not unless someone finds us, or we come to a water hole," said Uncle Richard. "Don't expect either. Our best bet is to keep going. Move it."

They walked on. Stephen saw something ripple in the distance. "Look!" he shouted, and pointed to the wet pool he saw on the horizon. He knew it was water.

"Wait—" Uncle Richard said.

Stephen raced toward the spring. He forgot how dry he was. The nearness of water gave him new strength. His footsteps pounded against the desert floor, but the pool looked as far away as ever. He sprinted on. The pool kept moving away from him.

At the bottom of a dune Stephen dropped to his knees. His hands grabbed some sand, but it sifted through his fingers and returned to the desert.

There was no water. The pool was a mirage.

Stephen kneeled there for minutes, staring at the sand. Finally Uncle Richard gripped Stephen's shoulder and lifted him to his feet.

"Move it," Uncle Richard said hoarsely. He dug a penny from his pocket and handed it to Stephen. "Put this under your tongue. It'll make your mouth water, so you won't be so thirsty."

A slight breeze wafted over them. Stephen felt cooler. The sunlight burned across his eyes, half-blinding him. How long had they marched? Stephen glanced at his watch. It had no meaning here. He saw the desert as if he were looking through a wide-angle lens. The dunes stretched everywhere. His feet moved forward, but he didn't seem to be getting anywhere.

"*I give up*," he said. "I can't give up." He kept walking.

The breeze got stronger, billowing the sand into little clouds around his shoes.

"Steve!" his uncle shouted. "Come back here!"

Stephen turned slowly. Two figures wavered a few paces behind him. He snapped his head up suddenly, waking himself, and rubbed his eyes. "What's the matter?"

Uncle Richard was sniffing the air. He had a wary, wolfish look in his eyes as he gazed around. To Lorelei he said, "There's no shelter. We'd better think of something quickly."

Then, turning to Stephen, he said, "Sandstorm coming up."

Stephen stared at the desert. He saw nothing but the billows of sand. Puzzled, he asked, "Where?"

Something that felt like a tiny knife grazed his cheek. In seconds the breeze became a wind. Stephen watched as the sand swirled on the earth and tore loose. It rose up on the wind as if possessed by an evil spirit.

"Get down!" Uncle Richard ordered. "Cover your mouth and nose and close your eyes!"

Lorelei and Uncle Richard dropped Jack Hartford.

Stephen would have thought the actor was already dead, but an irregular rise and fall of his chest showed life was still in him. Lorelei ripped a sleeve from Hartford's shirt and tied it over his mouth.

"He doesn't have much longer," she said. "We're running out of time."

"In more ways than one," Stephen said.

Tiny grains whipped into Stephen's face and arms, stinging him. He threw himself to the ground, facedown, with his hands cupped over his nose and chin. The sky was brown with dust. The sun that had tortured him was gone in the torrent of sand.

Slowly he realized that the sand was covering him. The weight of it pressed him to the ground. Stephen wanted to rise, to run, but there was nowhere to go. The wind roared in his ears. He frantically struggled to keep his head above the shifting sand, but it filled his mouth and choked him. He spat it out. More sand rolled over him.

As suddenly as it had started the roar died down.

I'm dead, Stephen thought. But he didn't feel

dead. His skin smarted where the granules had struck him.

Then he knew he was buried alive. The storm had raised a new dune with him under it.

He opened his mouth to scream, but sand poured into it, and he snapped it shut. The moment of panic was over. I've got to dig myself out, he decided.

Stephen tried to get up. The sand held him down. His hand brushed it aside, but more slid in to fill the hole he made. In desperation he thrust his arm up, driving through the dune.

His hand emerged into the warm air. Now he could dig.

He pulled himself free of the dune moments later. He felt the sun beat down on his face and smiled. "Uncle Richard," he called out. "I'm okay."

No one answered. Uncle Richard, Lorelei, and Jack Hartford were nowhere to be seen.

Stephen called his uncle's name again. He was no longer sure where they had been, because the desert had changed completely. Walking outward in a spiral from where he had been buried, Stephen searched for traces of his uncle and friends.

Glass glinted in the sunlight. At first Stephen thought it was the sand. Then he realized it was square.

Uncle Richard's watch!

Near the glass Uncle Richard's fingers broke through the dune. He sat up, shaking the dirt from his hair, and pulled Lorelei into the light.

Between them they picked up Jack Hartford again.

"Are you all right?" Uncle Richard asked Lorelei.

"I could use a bath," she said, trying to smile.

"We'll be lucky if we ever take a bath again," Stephen said.

"We've come about twelve miles," Uncle Richard said as they staggered on. "We can't be far from civilization now."

"Just our luck, we'll run into Ali Ben Kir," Stephen muttered. "We're not going to have to eat raw lizards or anything to survive, are we?" As his stomach churned from the thought, he remembered all kinds of old movies where the hero did just that.

For the first time all night, Uncle Richard laughed. "Yuk! Sounds pretty grisly to me," he said. "Tell you what, Steve. Bring it up again if we're out here a couple more days, okay? I'm not ready for raw lizards yet."

"Water!" he cried. There was a gleam in the desert ahead of them. But he remembered the mirage, and his heart sank. "No, it's just more sand," Stephen muttered.

But the water didn't back away as they approached. "You're wrong, Stephen," Lorelei said. "That's a *real oasis*!"

They made it to the oasis in minutes. A few small shrubs grew around the water hole. Stephen and Lorelei dropped to their knees, almost throwing themselves into it.

Lorelei raised the water to her cracked lips in her cupped hand.

Uncle Richard's arm flashed out, striking her in

the wrists. The liquid flew from her hand, and soaked into the dry ground.

Her eyes flashed with anger. "What was that for?" she growled.

Uncle Richard pointed into the desert. A few dozen yards from the pool, birds littered the sand.

"They're dead," Stephen said. He threw the water from his hand.

"We don't know that the water killed them," Lorelei said.

"We can't take the chance," Uncle Richard replied.

Lorelei stood and nodded. "Let's get going," she said. Her voice was sullen.

"Can you make it, Steve?" Uncle Richard asked.

"Sure," Stephen answered. I wish I was as certain as I sound, he thought.

"I thought you'd have a plan by now," Lorelei said to Uncle Richard.

"Oh, I have a plan," Uncle Richard answered. There were times he had the look of an angelic little boy, all brightness and innocence. "We move it."

They walked on, it seemed to Stephen, for miles.

Lorelei was the first to fall. "I can't take another step," she said. "You'll make it. Come back for me."

Uncle Richard grasped her under the elbow and helped her walk. When her legs would no longer respond, he dragged her in one hand and Jack Hartford in the other.

Stephen didn't see the ground anymore. It had become a yellowish blur. His feet had given up hurting. "Just one more step," he kept telling himself until it became the only thing he could think of.

Then Uncle Richard fell.

"Keep going!" he shouted to Stephen.

Stephen tromped ten more steps and collapsed. He lay at the bottom of a huge dune and stared up at it.

The desert had beaten them.

11

THE TABLES TURN

SUNDAY: 6:10 A.M., *Al-Karesh*

Funny, Stephen thought. All I wanted to do this weekend was watch *The Caves of Gold* a few hundred times.

The wind whistled in his ears. I'm so far gone I think I hear movie noises . . . somebody yelling . . . I didn't know you could hear mirages too. He sprawled under the harsh sun, waiting for the end to get him.

Suddenly his eyes shot open. I do hear something, he thought. A few voices drifted over the rise. They were arguing. Then a man shrieked, "Cut!"

Stephen's legs wobbled as he stood. His ankle turned and he fell.

On hands and knees he worked his way to the crest of the dune. On the other side, at the bottom, Clyde Lancer was bullying a group of actors.

They're shooting a scene, Stephen thought. We

almost made it to the movie set, and we didn't even know it.

Laughing to himself, Stephen stood. "Hey!" he shouted as he stumbled down the dune. His voice was a soft, hoarse croak. Frantically he waved his arms and shouted again.

On the set, heads turned to look at the little figure lumbering toward them.

As people ran to him the world twisted in front of Stephen. Then darkness gripped him, and he tumbled to the ground.

Stephen's eyes flickered.

He lay on a cot. A strong, sickening smell filled the air, and he wrinkled his nose at it. Ammonia, he thought. Where am I?

"Hi there, hero," Lorelei said from the next cot.

"Hero? Me?" said Stephen. He didn't feel like one—heroes didn't ache all over. His eyes focused, and he saw he was in a tent. Two cots over, Jack Hartford was unconscious, with an oxygen mask over his mouth.

Stephen sat up. Uncle Richard was nowhere around. "Where's Uncle Richard?" he asked.

"Right here, Stephen," Uncle Richard said. He walked into the tent followed by a doctor with little square glasses and graying hair.

"You should be lying down," the doctor said. "You're exhausted, and you ought to take care of that gouge in your scalp."

"No time," Uncle Richard curtly replied. "Jack's

slipping fast. We can't afford to lie around. Ready to move?''

"I think so," Stephen replied.

Lorelei sat up and shook herself awake. "I can't believe it's morning already."

Uncle Richard glanced at his watch. "We have twelve hours to get home. That ought to be enough."

"Enough?" Stephen shouted. "We'll never make it. Mom'll kill us. Come on, we've got to go." He could see from his uncle's face that they weren't leaving.

"Come on!" Stephen said again.

"What about Jack?" asked Uncle Richard.

Jack! Stephen thought. "He'll be okay. Lorelei can get a bunch of people together and go get Ali Ben Kir and save Jack. . . ." Even as he said it, Stephen knew it wasn't true.

"Okay," he said finally. "Let's help Jack. We won't have any trouble getting home before Mom and Dad." He knew that wasn't true either.

"Good," Uncle Richard said. He looked around the tent, studying the medical supplies with great interest. "Do you have any chloroform?" he asked the doctor.

The doctor slid off his glasses and wiped them on his tie. "Some. What do you need it for?"

"We're throwing a party," Uncle Richard said. "Let's go, Steve."

"Wait for me," Lorelei cried as they stepped from the movie tent. "You don't think I'm bailing out on you at this stage of the game?"

Uncle Richard poked his head back into the hospital tent. "You rest up. We'll need you later," he said. The boyish smile reappeared on his face. "I have a plan."

"What now?" Stephen muttered. Uncle Richard led the way as they jogged across the compound toward the makeup and wardrobe tent. Clyde Lancer puffed out to meet them.

"So what's with Hartford?" he said, panting. "I thought you were going to get him out of trouble."

"We're trying to save Jack's life," Stephen said, almost spitting in anger.

Lancer patted him on the head and turned to Uncle Richard. "Life, schmife. I've got a film to make here. These delays are going to drive me out of business. Every day we sit around costs my investors twenty-thousand dollars. Another couple of days like this and they'll shut down the picture."

"The problem," Uncle Richard said, "is that Ali Ben Kir is the key to the whole thing. He knows what kind of poison is killing Jack. It's probably of his own design, and he knows who killed Stone, if he didn't do it himself.

"Are the other actors any good?" Uncle Richard continued, walking into the tent with Stephen and Lancer behind him.

"The best," Lancer said. "Why?"

Uncle Richard riffled through dozens of costumes hanging on racks before answering. After a quick look, he pulled out two bedouin outfits, one for a man and one for a boy. "Because their lives, and ours, will depend on it. Our little drama has to be totally believable to Ali Ben Kir. Are you still holding Yusef and the giant?''

"Yeah," Lancer replied. "*What* little drama?''

Uncle Richard wrapped a scarf around his face and looked at his reflection in the mirror. "Not bad," he said. "A little work on the eyebrows, some dark skin tone . . . We're going to let Yusef and his friend go. Very carefully, of course.''

The desert clothes fit him perfectly. "You'd better get into your outfit if you want to join me, Steve.''

"Won't that be dangerous for the boy?" asked Lancer.

"Not if Ben Kir doesn't know who we are. And if he found out before we were ready to let him know, everywhere would be dangerous. So I'd rather have him with me where I know he's safe," Uncle Richard said. "By the way, did you know there's a valuable treasure buried deep below this camp?''

"No," Lancer replied. "I didn't.''

"Neither did Ali Ben Kir." Uncle Richard grinned. "I can't wait to *tell* him.''

Ten minutes later, crouched behind one of the tents, Stephen would not have recognized himself. Like Uncle Richard, he wore a long, loose robe over his body, and a cowl tied with scarves covered most of his head. Greasepaint tinted his hands and forehead. Anyone would have thought Stephen came from Al-Karesh.

Two actors dressed as security guards appeared, leading Yusef and the giant before Clyde Lancer.

The twisted Yusef had his hands tied behind his back, but the giant was chained hand and foot. He could barely move.

"I'm not sure what to do with you," Stephen heard Lancer say to the bandits. He strutted back and forth before them, looking important. The giant trained his eyes on the ground, but Yusef watched Lancer like an evil hawk.

They were interrupted by sounds of fighting and screaming from the other side of camp. Two actors dragged an Arab into the clearing, and forced him to his knees at Lancer's feet.

It was Uncle Richard in disguise.

Stephen fingered the sword that sat beside him. He waited for his cue. One actor grabbed Uncle Richard's wrist and squeezed. The hand opened. In it were two rubies.

"This guy has found out about the treasure," the actor said.

Yusef's eyes opened wide.

"Shut up," Lancer snapped. "Do you want to tell the whole world?" He reached down and lifted Uncle Richard's head until he was eye-to-eye with him. "How did you find out about this?"

Uncle Richard rattled off a stream of words. They seemed to be in another language, but Stephen realized that Uncle Richard was speaking English. It was garbled by the thick accent he used.

Stephen grabbed the sword and bolted, howling, for the clearing. Actors moved in to grab him, but he swung the sword in circles, driving them back. Uncle

Richard screeched words at him. Stephen threw the sword to him. One actor leaped to intercept it. Grabbing the sword, Uncle Richard cuffed the actor behind the ear with the hilt of the weapon.

Yusef was on his feet. "Come with me if you desire protection," he whispered to Uncle Richard. Stephen and his uncle raced across camp with the twisted man. Behind them the giant also tried to rise. Actors piled on top of him, pressing him down until he gave up the struggle.

The three fugitives reached the jeeps. "Do you know how to drive?" Yusef said.

"Yes," Uncle Richard replied. The thick accent masked his voice.

An actor appeared with a gun and fired it at Uncle Richard. The sword whirred up. A sharp spanging noise echoed off it. Even though Stephen knew it was a trick, it looked to him as if Uncle Richard had knocked a bullet out of thin air. Yusef's jaw dropped in amazement.

"I know someone who will pay you well for your services," Yusef said as they fled toward town in the jeep. He bit the rubies as if he were trying to make sure they were real. "And your knowledge of treasures."

A few minutes later they were in town.

"You will wait here," Yusef said. They were parked in front of a dingy café with men inside waving fans to drive away the heat and the flies.

"That's the jail across the street," Stephen said to his uncle when they were alone. "This guy is bold."

"He's pretty smart too," Uncle Richard warned. "When we get to see Ali Ben Kir, I'll do the talking. Don't say anything. You haven't got the practice it'll take to pull this off."

Two burly men appeared on either side of them. "Come with us," one said, and put his hand on Uncle Richard's sword. Uncle Richard pulled away. Growling, the man tore the sword from his hand.

Inside, at the back of the café, they were presented to Ali Ben Kir. He raised a thick finger to his temple. "You helped my man, Yusef. For that I am grateful. He tells me you are expert with the sword." When Uncle Richard said nothing, Ali Ben continued, "A thousand pardons. Do you speak English?"

"A little, yes," Uncle Richard answered. The words sounded clumsy and foreign.

"Let me see your faces," Ali Ben Kir said.

Stephen's heart jumped. Even in that light, they would be recognized. If that happened, they were doomed.

"It is not the custom of my people to remove our veils in public," Uncle Richard snapped.

The bandit chief's face went gray with anger. "We could remove them for you."

Uncle Richard crouched slightly, as if ready to spring. "Only if I were dead!" he hissed.

Ali Ben Kir shrugged and grinned. "Why speak of death, my new friend? Let us speak of better things— your treasure, perhaps."

A breath stopped in Uncle Richard's throat. With

feigned trembling, he said, "I know nothing of a treasure."

Ali Ben Kir leaned forward, staring Uncle Richard in the eye. "No, no, no," he said. "Tell me about the treasure."

"I know nothing," Uncle Richard repeated. A foot shot into his belly. He dropped to his knees and clutched his stomach. Rough hands seized his shoulders and held him down.

Ali Ben Kir clapped his hands, and a bandit stepped forward, carrying the sword that was taken from Uncle Richard. "The boy," Ben Kir said. "He is yours? Speak, dog."

"My—my sister's son," Uncle Richard gasped.

The bandit chief hissed, "The boy will tell us."

Ali Ben Kir raised the sword over Uncle Richard's neck, poised to strike.

12

TREASURE TRAP

SUNDAY: 8:55 A.M., *Al-Karesh*

"No!" Stephen yelled, trying to imitate his uncle's accent.

Ali Ben Kir sneered and signaled his man to lower the sword. "Tell me about the treasure, little one," the bandit chief said softly.

Stephen nodded and swallowed hard. His mouth was dry. Tell him! Tell him! he said to himself, but he couldn't speak more than a word at a time without giving himself away.

The bandit chief tapped his fingers impatiently. After several seconds he sighed and ordered, "Kill them."

"The American movie camp," Uncle Richard blurted. "Under it is a treasure."

"More," Ali Ben Kir commanded. He was unconvinced. "What treasure is this?"

"Th-the . . ." Uncle Richard stuttered. The more he stalled, the more interested Ali Ben Kir became. "How do you say? Much long time ago. Men from another land . . . Romans. They buried treasure. I will say no more."

Ben Kir's meaty paw struck him on the mouth. "Continue," the bandit barked, "or we will force the boy to tell us."

"Much jewels, gold coins," Uncle Richard said. "We look. Americans have much jewels already. Gold not found."

The bandit chief stroked his chin and pondered the information. "You know where the gold is?"

Uncle Richard shook his head. "On movie camp. The Americans, they not let us look."

"How did you plan to find this gold?"

"Map," Uncle Richard said. "We kill man for it."

Ali Ben Kir rolled his tongue inside his cheek. "Where is the map?"

Fake sobs burst through Uncle Richard. "The Americans. My map they stole. My beautiful map."

Clapping his hands, the bandit chief called for Yusef. The twisted man appeared from the shadows. "Gather all the men. Make them ready for battle. We go to fight the Americans."

The man with the sword tapped Uncle Richard with it and asked, "These?"

"Take them somewhere and dispose of them," Ali Ben Kir replied.

After tying their wrists, Ali Ben Kir's men dragged

Stephen and Uncle Richard down a narrow hall. A door opened and the sun flooded over them. The street behind the club was empty.

Bony fingers lifted up a metal grating. The stench of sewage stung Stephen's eyes. That's where they're dumping us, he thought.

Uncle Richard turned suddenly to face the man with the sword. "A curse on you," he snarled, and spat at the man.

The bandit shivered with rage. The sword whizzed forward, plunging into Uncle Richard's chest. He dropped away from the blade and plummeted into the sewer. With a cold sneer the bandit knocked Stephen in after him.

The grating clanked back over the hole. Voices trailed into the distance, and Stephen saw no one. "Uncle Richard," he said, "you can get up now."

With a laugh his uncle sat up, unhurt. "They bought it?"

"Yeah. That trick sword! I nearly had a heart atttack when that guy stabbed you with it. Why didn't we just tell Ali Ben Kir what he wanted to know?"

Uncle Richard pressed his fingers into the damp dirt wall. "I know his type. The more we refused to tell him, the more he believed us when we finally spilled the beans. Don't worry, Steve. You handled it like an old pro." Like a spider, he crawled up the wall, making his own handholds until he reached the grating.

One hard shove, and it was off the hole. Uncle Richard pulled Stephen to the surface.

They ran to meet Lorelei. She sat in a jeep parked next to the jail, counting the thugs who entered Ali Ben Kir's café.

Making sure that no one was watching, Stephen and Uncle Richard darted for the jeep. They were halfway across the street when Yusef stepped out of the club. Uncle Richard pulled a coin from his pocket and threw it at the bandit. It fell short, rolling past Yusef's feet. The coin glinted and the twisted man snatched it off the street. By the time he looked at the jail, the street was empty.

Speeding back to camp, Lorelei said, "That was pretty good. You know how to take care of yourself." She eyed Uncle Richard with interest.

"Are you going to be around for long after Jack's back on his feet?" she asked Uncle Richard.

"If there's time," he answered. He smiled mysteriously.

Stephen's heart jumped. The time! The hours were racing by. He thought of his mother, arms folded, stamping her foot as he walked in the door. What could he say? Hello, Mother. I've been on a little adventure in North Africa. He didn't want to think about it.

"The doc says Jack has forty-five minutes, maybe an hour, left," Lorelei was saying. "This plan of yours better work."

"My plans *always* work," said Uncle Richard. "*Almost* always."

Dozens of people were scurrying around the camp when they returned.

"We're all set," Lancer said as he met them.

Uncle Richard gazed over the camp. Men and women were digging holes in the sand at random spots, while others were running off into the dunes.

Stephen was startled to see that some of the extras were local people. He prayed they weren't in league with Ali Ben Kir. One look at their determined faces told Stephen they were pleased by this chance to stop the bandits who had plagued them for so long.

"They all have chloroformed swatches? They know not to breathe it themselves?" Richard said.

"When Clyde Lancer directs, people do what they're told," Lancer cried.

"You got the video stuff out of Jack's plane?" Stephen asked.

Lancer frowned. "Nice boy," he said to Uncle Richard, and patted Stephen on the head again. "I can tell he'll be a producer when he grows up."

"We better get started," Uncle Richard said. "Ben Kir and his men will be here any minute."

"Places everyone!" Lancer screamed through a megaphone. The entire camp stood still. "This is it. We have to do the scene right the first time, because there won't be a way to shoot it again. May I stress the word *shoot*!"

"They're all yours, Duffy," he said, handing the megaphone to Uncle Richard.

"Remember!" Uncle Richard shouted to the camp. "We're here to save Jack Hartford's life, not get ourselves killed. These men will be armed and dangerous, but if you play your parts, we'll pull this charade off.''

He dropped the megaphone. At the top of his lungs, he shouted, ''Move it!''

A soft buzz coming from the town filled the air. A lookout lowered his binoculars and cried, ''They're coming.''

Stephen, Uncle Richard, and Lorelei headed into the dunes. ''I brought your clothes,'' Lorelei said. ''The ones you're wearing reek like a sewer.''

''Rub in the sand as you change,'' Uncle Richard told Stephen. ''That'll absorb the smell.''

They slid out of sight as the first jeeps drove onto the movie set. Stephen peeped over the crest of the dune to watch. Armed thugs were leaping from the jeeps and pulling guns on the startled actors, herding them into the center of camp. After everyone was rounded up, one last jeep rolled in.

Ali Ben Kir had arrived.

''There's about thirty guys,'' Stephen said, ''plus Ali Ben.'' He looked at the dunes. They looked undisturbed, but hidden among them were twenty people from the movie crew.

Ali Ben Kir said to Clyde Lancer, ''I want the Roman treasure.''

Lancer shot back, ''It's *my* treasure.''

Ben Kir gripped the director's jaw in a huge hand. ''*My* treasure. The map, please.'' Lancer reluctantly pulled it from his coat pocket. It looked old, with tears and cracks across the paper.

"Where?" Ali Ben Kir asked, tightening his grip on Lancer.

"It—it doesn't say, exactly," the director blubbered. "We're digging now. Please, don't hurt me."

Ali Ben Kir tossed Lancer aside, as if he were a doll. "Let them continue digging," he told his men. "If they refuse, kill them. I want any gold or jewels they find."

"You'll never get away with this," Lancer said, whining. "We're Americans."

"You are amusing, little man," Ben Kir replied. "This is my country. You may yet disappear"—he opened his hand and watched nothing rise from it—"as if you were never born."

The bandits scattered among the tents.

Uncle Richard waved his hand from a dune. The signal went from crewman to crewman. One by one they returned to the camp, staying hidden behind the tents. "We had better get down there too," Uncle Richard said. He checked his watch. "There's twenty minutes to save Jack's life."

13

THE DEEP, DARK SECRET

SUNDAY: 11:05 A.M., *Al-Karesh*

The air seemed impossibly still as they wandered between the tents. People were moving all around but Stephen was aware only of the sound of his own breathing. He wished it were quieter, and prayed that the bandits wouldn't hear him.

He froze as a tent flap was suddenly pulled open.

The bandit's eyes flared when he saw Uncle Richard. He was holding the sword Uncle Richard had carried into town. A whistling streak split the air as the sword arched at Uncle Richard.

To the bandit's horror, the sword crumpled on Uncle Richard's arm. He opened his mouth to scream. Uncle Richard socked him, and the bandit collapsed in the dust.

"Watch it," Lorelei said. "We can't get discovered now."

Out of the corner of his eye, Stephen saw the bandit push off the ground, trying to stand. He began to moan softly. Stephen pulled a wet cloth from his back pocket and pressed it to the bandit's nose. The man hit the street like a brick.

"I must be losing my touch," Uncle Richard said. "They used to *stay* down when I hit them. Get his clothes, Lorelei."

"At least your idea of putting them to sleep with chloroform works," Stephen said as he tucked the cloth away.

"It better work," Uncle Richard said, "or we're in big trouble." He looked at his watch. "Sixteen minutes left. Let's hope that Ali Ben Kir is on cue."

The bandit chief was pacing in the center of the compound. Clyde Lancer sat cross-legged at his feet and sobbed. "You are safe," Ali Ben Kir said, "as long as you are not lying to me."

Yusef bolted from one of the tents. "Ali Ben Kir!" he called. "Come quickly. Your own eyes must see this." The twisted man trembled.

Ben Kir heaved Lancer to his feet. "You have been holding out on me, eh?" he whispered. The edge on his voice made the words a threat.

"No! I swear . . ." Lancer began, but Ali Ben Kir was already tramping over to Yusef.

The twisted man pulled open a flap for his chief. Ali Ben Kir stepped into the twilight of the tent and cast his eyes about. "What is so important?" he said.

His eyes bulged and he began to sputter. At the back of the tent was a shadowed cot.

Lying on the cot was Jack Hartford.

Ali Ben Kir quivered. His chest heaved as he gulped air. Veins stood out on his head.

He spun and brutally smashed both hammy fists into Yusef, knocking the twisted man off his feet. "Richard Duffy," he breathed.

He stomped into the clearing, looking for Lancer. The director was gone. "Everyone dies," he muttered in anger. He kicked a tent in frustration.

"RICHARD DUFFY!" the bandit chief bellowed. Bandits from all over the camp rushed to his side as he raged. From one tent to another he went, tearing away the canvas and finding nothing.

"You're on," Uncle Richard said to Stephen, and then slipped away.

Stephen took a deep breath. He remembered being forced to act in a play at school, and how much he disliked it. And that was only for a grade, he thought. This is for my life.

Shaking, he walked into the clearing and said, "Hello."

Ali Ben Kir spun to face him. "Where is he, boy?" the bandit chief snarled. His fingers curled and uncurled in strangled fury as he stalked toward Stephen.

"No need to get tough," Stephen said. "I'll take you to him." I can't believe I'm acting nonchalant, he thought. It's a good thing he doesn't know I'm scared out of my wits.

Ali Ben Kir's jaw dropped as Stephen spoke, and for a moment the bandit chief stared at his hand. He noticed his flexing fingers for the first time and brought them under control. His lips formed a bland smile. He pressed his hands together and bowed to Stephen.

"Please," he said politely.

As if I have a choice, thought Stephen. I sure hope Uncle Richard knows what he's doing. He led the bandit to the largest tent. The band of thugs trailed them.

"Ali Ben Kir! Do come in," said Uncle Richard's voice. He was in Clyde Lancer's tent. Screening equipment lined one side of it. In the rear was a large dining table shrouded in shadow and spread with food and bottles. Behind it lounged a man in silhouette.

Ali Ben Kir bowed. "Richard Duffy," he said. "I keep killing you, and you keep coming back to haunt me." He sat at the table, poured a goblet of wine, and lifted it. "I salute you," he said.

"I take it you're not a religious man," Uncle Richard said.

The bandit chief smiled and shrugged. "My religion is the coin of the realm."

Uncle Richard poured wine into another goblet and set it down in front of him. "Do you remember the last time we met like this?"

"I had several years to remember," Ben Kir replied, scowling. "In jail. You should not have come back. This time I have won."

"Have you?"

"My men surround this place. You cannot escape."

"True," Uncle Richard said. "I see no way out. But we've had this conversation before."

"We will not have it again," Ali Ben Kir said. Stephen could see he was enjoying himself. "Both you and Hartford have paid the price for crossing me."

Uncle Richard toyed with his goblet, running his finger along its intricate markings. He looked worried. "That's why you killed Stone, isn't it? To get Jack in enough trouble so he had to call me to bail him out. Right?"

The bandit chuckled. "Stone? I had heard Mr. Hartford murdered him."

"He couldn't have. I checked it out." Uncle Richard leaned across the table and stared into the bandit's eyes. Stephen knew his uncle was bluffing. Does Ali Ben know? he wondered. "But you! You would be clever enough to lure me here. I got you put away. You're not the sort who would let something like that go unpunished."

Ali Ben Kir shrugged. "Perhaps . . ."

Uncle Richard sat back. "So satisfy my curiosity. Why Stone?"

The bandit glanced around the room. "You are too relaxed for a man who is to die. This is a trick," he said.

"Come here," Ali Ben Kir said to Stephen. "Stand beside your uncle. I wish to keep my eyes on you."

"Who are we going to tell? What kind of trick can we pull?" Uncle Richard asked. "You owe me the truth before I die."

Ali Ben Kir's eyes opened wide with delight. He roared with laughter. "You are audacious, Richard Duffy. If only my underlings had your gall." He laughed. "I am glad they do not." He looked at Richard speculatively.

"Perhaps you are right. You have given me a challenge, after all. That is not an easy thing to do," he said, pondering the idea. "I will tell you the truth."

He gulped his wine, and wiped a silk-covered arm across his mouth. "It is true that I planned to lure you here. I intended to slay Jack Hartford. Your sickening loyalty would have forced you to avenge his death."

Stephen read his watch. Only ten minutes remained in which to save Jack Hartford.

"Ian Stone was an accident," the bandit continued. "That fool, Yusef! He was looking for Jack Hartford that night on my orders. Stone was Hartford's stand-in, his double. He was wearing Hartford's clothes. In the dark . . . let us say that *anyone* could make the same mistake."

"Yusef killed Stone?" Uncle Richard said, shocked.

"It worked out for the best," the bandit replied. "You are here. I have won."

"I don't get it" Stephen blurted it out in spite of himself. "Why didn't you just kill Jack later? Why poison him?"

Ali Ben Kir sneered at Stephen. Turning to Uncle Richard, he said, "The boy is full of words, like his uncle."

If I get treated like a kid one more time, I'm going to kill somebody, Stephen thought.

"I'm curious about that too," Uncle Richard said. "I've never seen a poison that acted like that before."

"Two reasons," Ben Kir answered. "I wished to keep Hartford alive, to make sure you would come to me. But I needed to keep him silent. The poison was useful for that purpose." He eyed Stephen.

Stephen flinched.

"I also wished to test it. The poison is new to me." He pulled a small pouch from his pocket. "Perhaps we could try it on the boy."

Uncle Richard launched himself across the table. He slammed into Ali Ben Kir, knocking over the man and his chair. Using all his strength, Uncle Richard clamped his hands around the bandit's throat and pressed him to the floor.

To Stephen's alarm, Ali Ben Kir slowly forced his arm up, despite Uncle Richard's effort to hold him down.

Uncle Richard cried out. His strength was spent. Ali Ben Kir's big hand snapped out, throwing Uncle Richard back onto the table. He tried to rise, groaned, and slumped across the broken dishes.

Ali Ben Kir snapped his fingers. A dozen bandits rushed into the tent armed with rifles.

"Uncle Richard!" Stephen whispered, patting his uncle on the cheek. "Get up. Do something."

Ali Ben Kir refilled his goblet with wine. "There is nothing left he can do. Ready," he said to his men.

They raised their rifles.

"Aim," the bandit chief cried. He drained his goblet with a flourish. The bandits fixed their sights on Stephen and Uncle Richard.

"Fire," Ali Ben Kir said.

14

SPECIAL EFFECTS

SUNDAY: High Noon, *Al-Karesh*

Stephen gazed down the rifle barrels. The blood froze in his veins, and time stood still.

Darkness hovered around Ali Ben Kir. He was a towering shadow. Not even human, Stephen thought. We didn't stand a chance.

"Fire!" Ali Ben Kir shouted again.

The rifles swung toward him. "What are you doing?" he said to the bandits. There was no answer. *"Fools!"*

Enraged, he took a step toward them. The bolts on the rifles snapped back. His men were ready to shoot *him*. Ali Ben Kir collapsed in on himself and shrank. His eyes cast over the faces of his men for the first time. His mouth fell open.

One of the bandits was a blond woman.

"You got the tape?" Lorelei said to Stephen.

He nodded, and ran to a small dresser. He pulled the mirror away from it to reveal a compartment with the videotape machine from Jack Hartford's plane. A camera was propped up next to it, aimed into the room. Stephen switched off the recorder.

"That was Stephen's idea," Uncle Richard said. The bandit chief sank into a chair, staring at the camera with unbelieving eyes. Uncle Richard peeled a small microphone from under the table. "A hidden camera, recording everything you said. The police will be very interested in learning who *really* killed Ian Stone."

Something had gone dead in Ali Ben Kir's face. He looked like an old man. "My men?" The voice trailed off into silence.

"They're all right," Lorelei said. "But they'll have headaches when they wake up. We knocked them out with chloroform. Actors taking their places was a nice touch, I thought."

Stephen tugged at his uncle's sleeve. "What about Jack?" he said. He tapped his finger on his watch. "If the doctor is right, there's about eight minutes left."

Uncle Richard extended a hand to Ali Ben Kir. "The antidote," he demanded.

Life came back to Ali Ben's face as he raised his head. A smile formed on his lips. Stephen could see on his face the same look of victory he had seconds earlier, when he had ordered their execution.

"Let us bargain," he said.

"Forget it," Uncle Richard said.

The bandit chief leaned back and shrugged. "I have all the time in the world. Jack Hartford does not."

"Let us have him," Lorelei said. "We'll make him give us the antidote."

"Perhaps," Ali Ben Kir said. "But when? By the time you succeed, your friend will be dead." He tilted his head at the video equipment. "I am already caught for one death. What can another matter to me?"

"What did you have in mind?" Uncle Richard asked.

The bandit chief stood. He circled the room, paying no attention to the rifles that were aimed at him.

This is what he loves, Stephen thought. He wants to control.

Ali Ben Kir reached for the videotape. Stephen snatched it from the machine and backed away. "The tape," Ben Kir announced. "The antidote for the tape. The actor lives, and I am a free man."

"But then we're back where we started," Stephen said. "Jack still goes to jail for killing Stone."

"I care nothing about that," the bandit said. He blew on his fingernails and carelessly polished them on his silk jacket.

"Richard . . ." Lorelei said. Uncle Richard was already deep in thought.

"No deal," Uncle Richard said. "The antidote for your life, Ben Kir."

"What are you going to do?" the bandit asked. He

laughed. "You had the chance to kill me once. You didn't. Why should I think you will kill me now?"

"We might," Lorelei said, trembling with rage. Her finger squeezed the trigger of her rifle. It was aimed at the bandit's belly.

Then she threw the rifle to the floor with a growl. "I can't do it," she choked.

"Americans!" Ali Ben Kir said with contempt. "You are soft-hearted and foolish. If you threaten to kill me, I will make you kill me. Or you may accept my bargain. Which will it be?"

Stephen watched the numbers flash on his watch. Two minutes passed. His hands were damp from worry.

"He has us over a barrel," Stephen said. "We have to go along with him. There's no other choice."

"No deal," Uncle Richard repeated.

"Then kill me," the bandit said. He rose and started toward the exit.

"Hold it!" Uncle Richard commanded.

Ali Ben Kir stopped, but did not turn around. "Your friends may shoot me in the back. I would think nothing of doing such a thing. But you are too weak—you will not kill me."

"You don't understand," Uncle Richard said. "I have *already* killed you."

15

FINAL SCENE

SUNDAY: 12:40 P.M., *Al-Karesh*

Stephen gasped. This is a great time to start bluffing, he thought.

"You *lie*," Ali Ben Kir roared. Then his eyes widened and his face turned ash gray as he glowered at Stephen's uncle.

A small cloth sack dangled from Uncle Richard's finger. Stephen had seen it only once before. It held Ali Ben Kir's poison.

"I didn't attack you because you threatened my nephew," Uncle Richard told the bandit. "That was a ruse. I really wanted to get my hands on this bag. Fighting was the only way I could snatch it without you noticing."

He threw the bag to the bandit. Ali Ben Kir looked into it and groaned. The bag was empty.

"That last goblet of wine," Uncle Richard continued. "I poured the entire contents of that bag into it. I figure that's enough to take even you down for the last count."

"Liar!" Ali Ben Kir spat the word out, but Stephen could see that the bandit doubted himself.

"Come on, Ali," Uncle Richard said. "Didn't you feel how gritty the wine was? Isn't there an aftertaste in your mouth right now?"

The bandit rolled his tongue inside his mouth. He swallowed hard.

Uncle Richard moved closer and taunted him. "The poison's taking effect, isn't it? It's hard to breathe. Your heartbeat is unsteady." Ali Ben Kir slapped his paw to his chest. His lower lip quivered, and water formed at the corners of his eyes.

"No . . ." he murmured. "No . . ."

"Now your vision is beginning to blur." The large man blinked and rubbed at his eyes. "Your fingers are going numb, and you can't feel the ground under your feet? Isn't that how it is?"

Ali Ben Kir flexed his hands and rubbed them together. He swayed slightly, as if his legs were giving out.

"*Isn't it?*" Uncle Richard demanded.

The bandit chief screamed. Suddenly he pulled at a cord that hung around his neck. A tiny bottle dangled on the end of the cord. Desperately he tore the cork from the bottle and raised it to his lips.

Uncle Richard dived across the room and snatched the bottle from the bandit. Ali Ben Kir swung wildly. Uncle Richard stepped inside the punch and jabbed his elbow into Ben Kir. The bandit collapsed to the floor and clutched his stomach.

"Please . . ." he moaned. "The antidote . . . please."

"Take this to Jack," Uncle Richard told Stephen. He slapped the cork into the bottle and handed it to the boy.

Stephen glanced at the fallen bandit. "Shouldn't we give him some?"

"Move it!" Uncle Richard barked. Like a shot Stephen dashed through the camp. Around him actors and crew chanted, "Go! Go! Go!" He wished he had been better in gym class. Everything seemed to be in slow motion as he barreled toward the hospital tent. Blood pounded in his ears, counting off the seconds.

I've got to make it, Stephen told himself. I'm not going to make it.

He burst into the tent and wheezed for air. Jack Hartford rested on a table. Stephen didn't recognize him at first. His skin was sunken and blue and tight around his bones.

"For Jack," he panted. He held the bottle out for the doctor. "Antidote." The doctor took it and filled a syringe with the liquid. As Stephen sank breathlessly to his knees, the doctor injected the antidote into Jack Hartford.

"All we can do now is wait," the doctor said. He helped Stephen to his feet. "Go back to your uncle. I'll let you know if anything happens."

When Stephen entered Clyde Lancer's tent a moment

later, he was startled by a roar. Ali Ben Kir was rolling on the ground, curled into a ball. He cursed.

"Oh, my gosh!" Stephen said. "I forgot he needs the antidote too."

He was about to run back for it when Uncle Richard clamped a hand on his shoulder. "Don't worry about Ali Ben," he said. "He isn't dying."

"But the poison . . ." Stephen began.

"I didn't use any," Uncle Richard said. "The only thing I put in his wine was flour."

"Filthy liar!" the bandit chief wailed. "I hurt. My hands have no feeling in them. I have all the signs of poisoning."

Uncle Richard shook his head. "No. When you saw the empty poison bag, you *believed* I poisoned you. You were ready to suffer any symptoms I told you to suffer."

Ali Ben Kir charged like an enraged bull. The bandit slammed his head into Uncle Richard, knocking him over. Stephen ducked away as Ali Ben grabbed for him.

Uncle Richard rolled away from those huge hands. The bandit chief's fist pounded a small crater into the ground where Uncle Richard had been. The next blow clipped Uncle Richard on the side of the jaw. He flew back onto the table, scattering dishes and food. Ali Ben Kir rushed in for the kill.

The actors took aim. "No," Uncle Richard shouted before they could shoot. "I'll take him." He reached back, grabbed a chair, and swung it.

With a crack the chair splintered on Ali Ben Kir's

shoulder. The big man halted and wiped the sawdust from his eyes. His lips curled back in a snarl, and Stephen saw the bandit's small, sharp teeth. He was like an animal now, showing bared fangs to an enemy.

Uncle Richard backflipped off the table. As Ali Ben Kir swung again, Stephen's uncle tucked a shoulder under the table and pushed upward. Table and fist smacked together. Ali Ben Kir screamed.

He watched in pained silence as his thick fingers swelled. The hand was useless, a pulpy mass.

Sobbing, Ali Ben Kir threw himself recklessly forward. His apish arms wrapped around Uncle Richard's waist. They plunged backward, tearing through the canvas on the tent and landing on the ground outside. Ali Ben Kir squashed the wind out of Uncle Richard.

Stephen saw something click in his uncle's face, something he had never seen before. It no longer had any sign of thought or emotion. His eyes stared blankly forward.

Uncle Richard's fist snapped up and struck Ali Ben Kir.

For long minutes they stood in that position. Ali Ben Kir kept squeezing Uncle Richard in that powerful bear hug. Uncle Richard swung his fists, pounding the bandit as hard and as often as possible. Ali Ben Kir never flinched.

Finally, spent, Uncle Richard rolled up his eyes and slumped back in Ali Ben Kir's arms.

Ali Ben Kir leered down at his fallen enemy and loosened his grip.

Uncle Richard's hands looped up. He cracked the heels of his hand into Ali Ben Kir's neck.

The bandit fell back, clawing at the pain in his head. Uncle Richard staggered. His teeth grit together. He focused on Ali Ben Kir and clasped his hands together.

With a fierce swing Uncle Richard smashed both fists into Ali Ben Kir. The bandit toppled into the sand and stayed there.

"Uncle Richard!" Stephen cried. "Are you okay?" Uncle Richard swayed on his feet, and Stephen ran to prop him up.

"I will be when I catch my breath," Uncle Richard said. "This isn't my favorite way to spend a Sunday afternoon." Out of the corner of his eye he noticed a glint of light on a metal barrel. As a gunshot roared, Uncle Richard fell, pulling Stephen under him.

Yusef stood there, holding a smoking rifle. He glared in hatred at the men on the ground.

He aimed his rifle at Ali Ben Kir.

"You! Great man!" he cried. "You lie to Yusef. You betray Yusef. We do your bidding, you say we are unbeatable! Hah! Look now. You are nothing. Nothing!" Tears dribbled down his cheeks. His words rolled and broke on choked sobs.

"Drop it," Lorelei said. She had her rifle aimed at Yusef. He trembled and his finger tightened on the trigger of his gun.

Yusef threw the gun into the sand. The actors swarmed over him, holding him still. He fought long enough to spit on Ali Ben Kir, and gave up.

Stephen and Uncle Richard stood. "You're quite the tiger when you want to be," Uncle Richard told Lorelei.

"You're not so bad yourself," she replied. The crew carried away Ali Ben Kir and his henchman. "I guess that just about wraps things up."

"About time too," Stephen sighed. "We're going to have real trouble getting to New York before it's too late."

"Mr. Duffy! Lorelei!" Clyde Lancer called out. He huffed toward them, his face white with shock and grief.

"Calm down, man!" Lorelei said. "What's the matter?"

Lancer's head drooped. He couldn't look them in the eye. "We were too late," he whimpered.

"Jack Hartford is dead."

16

"THE END"

SUNDAY: 1:15 P.M., *Al-Karesh*

Jack Hartford's body rested on a green cot.

"If he had received the antidote a few minutes earlier, we might have saved him," the doctor said. "There's no way to know without tests. There was no way for you to know."

"He was great," Stephen said. Tears trickled from his eyes.

"Sorry, Jack," said Uncle Richard. "I let you down." Stephen saw that his uncle, too, was holding back tears.

Clyde Lancer shook his head. "The finest action hero the silver screen ever knew, and he didn't even finish two pictures. What a waste. We may never see his like again."

Uncle Richard pulled a sheet up over Hartford. He paused to study the actor's face. "He almost doesn't look dead. It's hard to believe. Good-bye, pal.''

A single tear rolled down Stephen's cheek. He had never even gotten Hartford's autograph. The sheet went over Jack Hartford's head.

"I'm sorry I ever thought he killed Stone," Lorelei said as they filed out of the tent. "Too bad I didn't get the chance to know him better."

"These things happen," Lancer said to Lorelei and Uncle Richard. "No one is blaming you two. You did your best." They said nothing.

Stephen stayed behind, thinking about Jack Hartford. His was the first dead body he had ever seen. He thought of *The Caves of Gold*. Hartford laughed and swaggered through the story, overcoming deathtrap after deathtrap, saving the day, getting the girl. That was how things were supposed to work out. That's movies, Stephen thought. This is real life. I'm old enough to know that.

I prefer the movies. "Thanks, Jack," he said in a soft voice. "You made me happy for a while."

"Steve! Are you coming?" Uncle Richard called. "We have a plane to catch."

"I'll be there in a minute," Stephen yelled back.

A wrinkle in the sheet moved.

Stephen wasn't sure he saw it. It's like on the desert, he decided. The mirages. You see what you want to see.

He almost didn't notice that the sheet twitched again.

He's alive, Stephen thought.

"He's alive!" The words burst form Stephen in a shout. Within seconds the tent was filled with people.

Stephen told them what he saw. "Impossible," the doctor insisted. "Just reflexes." He dabbed at Jack Hartford's chest with a stethoscope. "No heartbeat. This man is dead."

"Wait!" Uncle Richard said. "I've seen things like this before. In the Congo. Mau Maus use drugs that make a man look dead. Even doctors can't tell the difference. Maybe Ali Ben Kir's poison was like that."

He snatched the stethoscope from the doctor and pressed it to Hartford's chest. Nothing. Seconds passed. "It's been a quarter of a minute," the doctor said. "I'm sorry, but you may as well give up."

A faint thump sounded on the stethoscope.

"I've got a heartbeat!" Uncle Richard cried. "Give him something to make his heart work faster." The doctor stood there with a puzzled look.

"Move it!" Uncle Richard ordered. The doctor snapped into action, fumbling with syringes. Finally he drove a needle into Jack Hartford's chest.

"Adrenalin," he said. "It should work if anything will."

Uncle Richard listened again to Jack's heart. The pulse was growing stronger, louder. As the pulse speeded up, the actor's chest pumped up and down.

"Come on, you lousy pilot," Uncle Richard said as he slapped Jack Hartford on the cheek, trying to rouse him. "You can do it, Jack!"

"You can do it!" Stephen joined in. The excitement gripped him so hard, he could barely breathe. "You can do it!" The chant spread through the room. The entire camp was a cheering section, calling Jack Hartford back to life.

"Can't a guy get some privacy around here?" Jack Hartford mumbled.

Fifteen minutes later Stephen and Uncle Richard were ready to leave for the airstrip. To Stephen's surprise, two men brought Jack Hartford to them. The actor was still weak, but the antidote was working quickly.

"I *really* want to thank you for everything," Jack said as he shook Uncle Richard's hand. They were at the edge of camp now, waiting for the car that would take Stephen and Uncle Richard to the airstrip. Jack sat comfortably in a wheelchair, with Lorelei beside him.

"The doc says I'll be all right after a good night's sleep. It seems he gave me enough antidote to keep me from kicking the bucket, but not enough to bring me around."

"Thank Steve," Uncle Richard said. "His sharp eyes saved you. I just did the dirty work."

"Anything I can do for you, you just ask," Jack told Stephen.

"Well . . ." Stephen said. "I would like to see *The Deep, Dark Secret*."

A twinkle gleamed in Jack's eye. "Tell you what, pardner. Any movie I'm ever in, you get an advance video of it, and all the free tickets you want. That's a promise."

"Wow!" Stephen said. For once, he was speechless. This is a dream come true, he thought. I can't wait to get home and start watching. . . .

He stiffened at the thought of home, and glanced at his watch. "Oh, no!"

"What's the matter?" Uncle Richard asked.

"Mom and Dad," Stephen groaned. "We'll never get home before them. I'm doomed." I wish this adventure could last forever, he thought. It would beat explaining this to Mom for the rest of my life.

Three policemen appeared from the camp, leading a familiar figure past Stephen and the others. "You are a worthy foe, Richard Duffy," Ali Ben Kir said as he passed. "Perhaps we will will meet again, in the future."

"I doubt it," said Uncle Richard. "You haven't got a future, Ali." Laughter brought crimson streaks to Ali Ben Kir's face.

"We shall see," he said, "next time." Then the police forced him into the back of a truck. The truck drove off, taking him to jail.

"Boy!" said Lorelei. "Some guys just don't take a hint, do they?"

"Ali Ben Kir will be put away for a long time," Uncle Richard said. "Maybe when he gets out, we can be old men playing checkers."

"I thought thirty or so *was* old," Stephen said. Everyone chuckled.

A car appeared in the distance. It was a limousine, specially equipped to drive across the desert. As it pulled up to the camp, Clyde Lancer stepped out of the car. "Like it?" he said. "It's a beauty. Property of the film company. It'll get you to the airstrip in record time." Lancer read the time. "Better hurry. You'll miss your connecting flight to Marrakesh."

Stephen was bewildered. "Aren't we flying home on Jack's plane?"

"That's a bit slow," Uncle Richard said. "Mr. Lancer was kind enough to rent a supersonic plane for us. We should be in New York a little before your parents get in."

Stephen couldn't believe his ears. "I'm saved," he said. He leaped into the car.

"So long, Jack," he called from where he sat. "It was really great meeting you. You, too, Lorelei."

Jack rolled his wheelchair to the car window as Lorelei and Uncle Richard said good-bye. "The pleasure was all mine, pardner. See you at the movies, right?"

"Right!" Stephen said. "Uncle Richard! We have to go!"

"Are you sure you can't stay for a while?" Lorelei asked Uncle Richard.

He sighed. "You heard Steve. He's the boss. Maybe next time . . ."

Lorelei smiled. "Consider it a date."

"*Uncle Richard!*" Stephen called.

A few minutes later the car pulled out of camp. Stephen looked back at the movie set. Jack Hartford was rolling his wheelchair back to his tent. Lorelei watched the car until it disappeared over the horizon.

17

TIME RUNS OUT

SUNDAY: 11:40 A.M., *New York*

"Coming into New York. Please fasten your seat belts," a voice said over the airplane loudspeaker. Uncle Richard stretched in his seat, coming out of a nap. Barely awake, Stephen watched a French film on the movie screen. He didn't like it. Too bad it didn't have more action, Stephen thought. Or Jack Hartford.

"There's a lot of traffic over the airport," the pilot said over the intercom. "We'll be circling, but only for a few minutes. I hope this doesn't cause any problems."

Uncle Richard picked up the microphone in the passengers' cabin and answered, "Not as long as we beat the noon flight from Boston."

Stephen looked out the window of the plane. Manhattan loomed below. To the south he could see the Statue of Liberty. The Empire State Building rose directly to the west. When Stephen saw the large patch of green called Central Park, he looked for his own block and his parents' house. From the air, all the buildings in his neighborhood looked the same.

A beeping announced that the pilot was coming onto the loudspeaker. "I checked the Boston flight," the pilot said. "It landed ten minutes ago."

Uncle Richard bolted up, suddenly alert. Stephen checked his watch. It read 11:42. "They're not supposed to get in for more than fifteen minutes," he said. "What are we going to do?"

"Don't panic," Uncle Richard said. His brow wrinkled with thought. "I have a plan."

He grabbed the microphone. "Swing back over Manhattan," he told the pilot. "Are there parachutes in here?"

"Parachutes?" Stephen said. He looked back at the city. It was all rock and metal. "We're not going to . . ."

"In the rear compartment," the pilot answered. "But you can't . . ."

"Slow down and get as low as you can," Uncle Richard barked. "We're jumping. Depressurize this cabin or a lot of it will go out with us." He ran to the rear compartment and pulled out two large white sacks.

"No way," Stephen said. "I'm not putting that on."

Uncle Richard pulled Stephen's right arm through a strap. "Don't be silly," he said. "Skydiving is easy." He peered out the window at the little buildings. "Which one of those is ours?"

"Oh, no," Stephen cried. The parachute pressed his knapsack into his back. "Can we aim parachutes that carefully?"

Uncle Richard rubbed his jaw. "Hmmm. I forgot you haven't had much practice at this. We'd better head for Central Park and run the rest of the way."

"I haven't had any practice at this at all!" Stephen moaned.

Pointing to a handle on Stephen's parachute, Uncle Richard said, "When you get out the door, count to ten and pull that." He turned the large wheel on the door and it swung open. Manhattan sprawled below.

Stephen stared at it. The cars in the streets crawled like insects from stop light to stop light. Mom and Dad are in one of those cars. "Maybe we shouldn't do this," he said.

"Start counting," Uncle Richard said. He shoved Stephen out the door and jumped.

Ten . . . nine . . . eight . . . Stephen thought as he plunged. The city rushed up at him. This isn't as bad as I thought.

Curled into a ball, Uncle Richard caught up with Stephen. In free fall, he spread his arms and legs and grabbed Stephen's free hand.

. . . seven . . . six . . . five . . . The cars were as big as toys now. Stephen laughed and reached out in fun, pretending to pick one up. This is great.

. . . four . . . three . . . two . . . Stephen's hands were damp. He quivered as the ground widened out to greet him. What if something goes wrong? He decided Uncle Richard wouldn't let anything happen to him.

. . . one! Stephen jerked the ripcord. It pulled away from the sack.

The parachute didn't open.

"Uncle Richard!" he screamed. His words were lost in the wind. Uncle Richard's hand tightened around his wrist and he was hoisted up.

Stephen grabbed on to Uncle Richard's belt and clung there. The parachute swooped out of Uncle Richard's sack. They jerked in the air as it opened and billowed above them.

Below them sprawled the green lawn of Central Park. *Home!* His knuckles whitened as he gripped Uncle Richard's belt. I hope I live long enough to enjoy it.

A crowd had gathered by the time they landed. Suddenly sirens tore the air and red lights flashed. Six Manhattan policemen sprang from black and white cars.

Leading them was a dumpling of a man with a round face. He rapped a nightstick in his hand and frowned. "It's against the law to parachute in this city. I'd like you to come to the station and discuss it if you could."

Uncle Richard turned with a grin on his face. "Right now, Matty, I really haven't got the time."

The policeman tilted back his hat in amazement. "Richard Duffy, you're on some sort of special mission, I suppose?"

"You *know* this guy?" Stephen asked his uncle.

"Oh, I know a lot of people," Uncle Richard replied. To Matty he said, "Could we get a lift from you? We're a bit pressed for time."

The policeman leaped into action. "All right, you folks, break it up," he told the crowd, and led the way to his car.

With sirens blaring and lights flashing, they sped through the Manhattan streets. Within minutes the patrol car turned onto East Sixty-first Street. It screeched to a halt in front of Stephen's home.

Stephen and Uncle Richard jumped from the patrol car and dashed up the stairs two at a time.

The police car roared off. Casually Uncle Richard turned the lock. The front door swung open. The house lights were off.

"Hello . . ." Uncle Richard said meekly. "There's no one home. We got here first."

"It doesn't matter," Stephen said. "Mom will take one look at us and figure out that something is going on. You don't *know* her like I do."

"She's my sister, remember?" Uncle Richard said. "Calm down, take a deep breath, and keep quiet. She won't know where we were or what we were doing. It'll be our deep, dark secret forever, okay?" He winked, and Stephen knew they'd be able to pull it off.

All the risks had paid off. Stephen sighed. Relaxing, he stretched and turned his head. He jumped.

A taxicab drove up the street. Stephen recognized

his mother in the back seat. She saw me, he guessed, and hoped he was wrong. "They're here," he said.

With a look of horror Uncle Richard pulled him into the house. The door slammed shut.

"Hi, there," Stephen's mother called as she entered. The house was silent. "That's funny," she told his father. "Maybe they're not home."

Dad laughed. "Maybe they took a weekend trip to Europe. I've always wanted to do that."

Mrs. Lane ignored him, and walked to Stephen's room. "Did you have a good weekend?" she said as she entered. Stephen lounged on his bed, eyes locked on his television.

"Okay, I guess," he answered.

"What did you do? Not watch TV all weekend, I hope."

"No, I did stuff," he said. "How was Boston?"

"Fine. A lot of people talking, really." She watched the moustached man on the TV screen. Another man sat in the shadows. He looked oddly familiar, but she couldn't recognize him. "Stephen," she said, "you must stop watching these silly movies. You're going to lose touch with reality."

Dad appeared in the doorway. "Anyone hungry?" he asked. "I was thinking of ordering some pizza."

Stephen rolled off the bed. "Great!" he cried, and walked toward the kitchen with his parents.

"So you and Uncle Richard got along okay?" Dad asked.

"Yeah," Stephen said. "He's a neat guy."

"Is someone talking about me?" Uncle Richard

called from the bathroom. Moments later he came out in a robe. He had a towel draped around his neck, and his hair was wet.

"Where have *you* been?" Stephen's mother said gravely, looking into his face.

"Wh-what do you mean?"

"Your face is so red! It wasn't like that on Friday. How did you get sunburned?"

"Oh!" he chuckled. "I fell asleep under a sunlamp at my health club yesterday. A silly thing to do."

"Honestly!" Stephen's mother said with disgust. "Maybe it isn't such a good idea to leave Stephen with you. You do have a hard enough time taking care of yourself."

"Him look after me?" Stephen said. "I thought you left *me* here to look after him." A withering frown from his mother silenced Stephen, but Dad laughed.

"Come on," Dad said. "Let's go pick up that pizza."

In Stephen's room the TV set played on. But Mrs. Lane was wrong. Stephen hadn't been watching a movie. Only Uncle Richard would have known that the face on the TV screen was the face of Ali Ben Kir, and that Stephen had brought home the videotape of the bandit chief of Al-Karesh confessing to the killing of Ian Stone.

RACE AGAINST TIME™

Join the race right at the start . . .
Become a RACE AGAINST TIME Adventurer NOW!

Your first top-secret assignment is to fill in the coupon below and join other fans of Stephen Lane and Uncle Richard in finding out more about the exciting world of RACE AGAINST TIME.

Yes, I would like to become a RACE AGAINST TIME adventurer.

Please send me FREE OF CHARGE:

(1) a RACE AGAINST TIME badge
(2) a membership card with my own personal code number
(3) a secret letter from Uncle Richard and Stephen

Name _____ Age _____

Address _____

_____

_____

I found out about RACE AGAINST TIME books

from _____

_____

Send to:
RACE AGAINST TIME,
Armada Paperbacks,
8 Grafton Street,
London W1X 3LA.

Australia, *send to:*
RACE AGAINST TIME,
Armada Paperbacks,
Wm. Collins Pty Ltd.
P.O. Box 497,
Sydney, N.S.W. 2000.

RACE AGAINST TIME

Adventure where *every second* counts!